The Worlds of Science & Religion

General editors of this book
and others in
the *Issues in Religious Studies* series:
Peter Baelz and Jean Holm

The Worlds of Science & Religion

DON CUPITT

HAWTHORN BOOKS, INC.
Publishers / NEW YORK

First published in Great Britain in 1976 by Sheldon Press, Marylebone Road, London NW1 4DU.

First published in the United States in 1976 by Hawthorn Books, Inc., 260 Madison Avenue, New York, New York 10016.

THE WORLDS OF SCIENCE AND RELIGION

Library of Congress Catalog Card Number: 75–41795
ISBN: 0–8015–8924–X
1 2 3 4 5 6 7 8 9 10

For John and Caroline

CONTENTS

The
Worlds
of
Science
& Religion

PREFACE

The issues summed up in the phrase 'science and religion' are many, and they have been central to Western thought for centuries. In the older books on the subject it is sometimes suggested that there are a limited number of points of conflict —such as miracles, Genesis, prayer, and the human soul—and that the problems are solved if only a settlement can be negotiated at each of these points in turn.

I have attempted a new approach, which brings the question of cosmology to the fore. In prescientific cultures the cosmology (or world-picture) represented the universe in such a way as to validate the public moral order, and tell men why they were here, how they should live, and what they could hope for. But our modern scientific cosmology refuses to perform this function, and it has destroyed the old religious cosmologies.

This book will, I hope, set you thinking about the fundamental spiritual dilemma of modern science-based industrial societies.

1

IN THE BEGINNING

'God made us, didn't he?', said four-year-old Caroline. 'Well, it's nice to think so', said five-year-old John judicially, 'but if you look at fossils and things you see it all came about by evolution. We just sort of grew gradually.'

Caroline was disturbed by this apparent conflict of rival answers, and John was visibly uneasy too. It was not that he had any doubts about his own answer (after all, he had real fossils in his bed, and knew all there was to know about dinosaurs), but it did not seem quite to meet Caroline's question. She was enquiring about an answer to the question, *Who made us?*, whereas John's reply took the form of an answer to a different question, *In what way did we, the human race, come to be?* What did it mean to reply to her by giving her the answer to a different question? Was there something wrong with the question she wanted answered? John's reply suggested that her question was somehow ill-framed, or based on a misunderstanding, or unanswerable, and needed to be rephrased.

At any rate, there was a pregnant pause, filled with an almost audible whirring and clicking. They appealed to me for a ruling. I was on the spot. 'Well, I think you're both right', I said, 'God made us, but he did it bit by bit, by evolution'; a reply which was at once diplomatic, orthodox and shallow.

I swear this exchange really took place, and that the ages of the children were as stated; and I was just as disconcerted as every other adult by the intellectual force of children. All children are precocious in that way. But, like a fool, instead of settling down to a leisurely argument, I changed the subject. Only now, years afterwards, can I try to make amends.

Caroline had heard, at playschool, about the doctrine of Creation. In the beginning the Lord God created all things in

1

heaven and earth. Everyone wants to know how it all began, and the answer that *God made us* (and, by implication, everything else) no doubt seemed at first to her, as to everyone, beautifully clear and satisfying. So what had led her to question it?

Interestingly, her doubt did not arise because of her knowledge of the facts of life. Nowadays even the youngest children have a fairly good understanding of the mechanics of sexual reproduction and the growth of the embryo in the mother's womb; and it might appear at first sight that such knowledge is a sufficient answer to the question about *Who made us?* Bertrand Russell, in debate with a believer in God, once complained, 'Every man who exists has a mother, and it seems to me that your argument is that therefore the human race must have a mother, but obviously the human race hasn't a mother'.[1] That is, Russell says the answer to *Who made us?* can be given only in terms of the facts of sexual reproduction, and that there is an obvious fallacy in looking for a Universal Parent over and above all the particular parents. The fallacy is called, in traditional logic, the Fallacy of Composition. You cannot safely deduce that, because every member of a class has a certain property, the class as a whole has that same property. Russell's point is one that had been made long before by David Hume:[2]

> Did I show you the particular causes of each individual in a collection of twenty particles of matter, I should think it very unreasonable, should you afterwards ask me, what was the cause of the whole twenty. This is sufficiently explained, in explaining the cause of the parts.[3]

So for Hume and Russell any explanation of the world has to be explanation bit-by-bit. They regard any request for overall or ultimate explanation as perpetrating the Fallacy of Composition. So, the answer to *Who made us?* is *Mother and father*; and

[1] John Hick, ed., *The Existence of God* (New York, Macmillan 1964), p. 175 from a B.B.C. discussion with Fr F. C. Copleston S.J., broadcast in 1948.

[2] David Hume (1711–76), Scottish philosopher and historian, was a leading exponent of empiricism, the doctrine that all our knowledge is derived from experience, especially sense-experience.

[3] David Hume, *Dialogues Concerning Natural Religion* (1779), Part IX.

the answer to *Who made them?* is, *Their mothers and fathers*, and so on. Why we are all here is sufficiently explained in terms of many particular acts of generation.

But the children would certainly not have been satisfied if I had replied along the lines suggested by Hume and Russell. They, and for that matter myth-making primitive men, knew all about the facts of generation, and yet still wanted to know, *Who made us?* Their enquiry was not a fallacious transfer to the universal level of an ordinary enquiry about generation. It was perfectly plain that they were asking about makings and beginnings in some different and more fundamental sense, and they were troubled by the seeming conflict between two different kinds of answer, one theological, the other in terms of a theory of biological development. One might convey what they were asking by contrasting the two questions, *How did I come into the world?* (answer, I was born of another human being by sexual reproduction) and, *How has there come to be a human race at all?* To this latter question Caroline proposes a theological answer, John an answer which invokes the facts of sexual reproduction, the idea of an immensely long period of time, and a biological theory of the origin of a new species. Both of them are enquiring about first beginnings, or remote beginnings, rather than proximate beginnings. But the past tense in John's answer is a different kind of past tense from the past tense in Caroline's answer.

Caroline's doubt about *God made us*, then, did not arise because she had learnt where babies come from. It had arisen because she had gathered that not everybody believes in God. I had overheard their mother explaining that some people believe in God, but others do not, and they must think it out for themselves as they grew up. Uneasy at the news that God was somehow optional, Caroline was seeking reassurance.

John's reply, 'It's nice to think so, but ...', shows that he was already doing philosophy. I had noticed that, like most children, he lived in two worlds, and was often concerned to decide into which world he should put a particular idea or belief. Into the beloved world of the imagination he had put talking animals, Father Christmas, the fairies who substitute a coin for the milk-tooth under the pillow, faith in the power of wishing and now, it seemed, belief in God. On the other side was the 'real' world

3

of empirical fact and of science. He felt very strongly drawn to both worlds, but felt it necessary to draw a clear line between them[4] and, though with regret, to admit the inferior status of the world of imagination.

It is not easy to find the right words for these two worlds, for they are both, in an important sense, equally 'real' to the child, and equally necessary to the development of the child's mind. It would be hard to imagine a childhood without such vitally-important ideas as those of mythic time ('once upon a time', 'far away and long ago'), and talking animals. At the very least, we seem to need imaginary worlds in order to get the 'real' world into focus. In the opening chapters of *Hard Times* Dickens portrayed, in Mr Gradgrind's modern day school, an education without imagination, and did so with unsurpassed hatred and contempt. We owe this rediscovery of the importance of the world of the imagination to what the mid-Victorians were beginning to call the Romantic Movement.

John was Victorian in the way he believed in two distinct worlds. Children are very excited by something that seems to link the two worlds, such as a robot (John drew an angel as a winged robot); a dinosaur (a historical *dragon* long ago); father dressed up as Santa Claus; or a real coin, which parents insist must have been put there by the fairies, under the pillow in the morning. Children like both worlds, and like to distinguish between them; but at the same time are thrilled by seeing intrusions from the make-believe world into the real world.[5] Is this the same thing as the answers to prayer, the divine interventions, the visions and portents, miracles and special providences of religion?

At any rate, John, by his 'It's nice to think so, but ...', was assigning statements about God to the make-believe world. To be more exact, for him theological statements are to scientific

[4] He once asked me, 'Did Jesus *really* rise from the dead?' To which of his two worlds should *that* belief be assigned?

[5] 'There is a curtain, thin as gossamer, clear as glass, strong as iron ... between the world of magic, and the world that seems to us to be real. And when once people have found one of the little weak spots in that curtain which are marked by magic rings ... and the like, almost anything may happen.' E. Nesbit, *The Enchanted Castle* (London, Ernest Benn 1960 edn), p. 250.

statements as the language of the world of imagination is to the language of the prosy everyday world. Religion is to science as poetry is to prose, and in line with the great tradition of hard-headed British philistinism he was saying that prose is true, whereas poetry is just pleasing fiction. It would be wonderful if the magic world were true, but it isn't, and it is an older brother's duty to grow up and put away childish things.

But I am not inclined to criticize John for taking this sober line, and assigning statements about God to the magic world. It is not a bad first approximation, and as I say, we are in many ways still Victorians, and in terms of the Victorian world-view it was the best he could do. I think the main reason why he put *God made us* into the magic world is that Creation's tense is mythic time ('in the beginning'), whereas he had grasped that the evolutionary process had occurred in the same time-order as our own birthdays and schooldays. There 'really' had been dinosaurs, because he had seen their bones in the museum.

Both children were clear that the two worlds differ in logical character. One of the main differences concerns coherence and the settlement of disputes. In the prosy real world one belief has to be consistent with another, anomalies can by and large be explained, and disputes can by and large be settled. There are answers, and there are authoritative people, books and so on; and when the right answer has been found it must simply be accepted. The make-believe world is not subject to such constraints. It is highly populous and disorderly. There is a riot of conflicting beliefs, many beliefs are optional, and things are true if you wish hard enough. Belief in God seemed, to John at least, more like belief in Father Christmas than like belief that the sun is made of burning gas. In the make-believe world the laws of nature are subordinate to the power of faith: the cartoon character continues running horizontally well beyond the cliff-edge, and it is only when he suddenly realizes that he is unsupported that his jaw drops, and he promptly plummets downwards. Is not that very illustration used as an allegory of the nature of religious faith in Matthew's Gospel (Matt. 14.28–31)? But that surely proves that religious faith belongs to the magic world rather than to the real world.

Though most children think in terms of two worlds, the form

5

this takes nowadays depends upon the rise of a new view of childhood, and a special literature for children, since the Romantic Movement. The main idea is that the child, in his development, recapitulates the history of the entire human race. The magic world is the primitive world. The youngest children, like the first men, live naturally in a world of poetry rather than prose, emotion and intuition rather than analytical reason, myth and magic rather than science. It is very striking how much the culture of early childhood is a reminiscence of the prescientific world-view. Prescientific man saw the world in terms of stories, and those stories survive yet in the magic world of childhood. Robin Hood and King Arthur, Hans Andersen and the brothers Grimm, the *Thousand and One Nights*, Moses in the bulrushes and the Nativity, the myths and folk-tales of Greeks, Northmen and Christians, were all once adult property, and are now given to children as a kind of crash course in the imaginative life of the past; so that the child, as he grows up, recapitulates the history of our culture.

In many popular writers, such as C. S. Lewis and J. R. R. Tolkien, personal nostalgia for childhood and scholarly affection for the myths, epics and sagas of the past have fused in the desire to write books for children; for children at least should be able to understand what the world was like before men grew up and lost their innocence. Here is a complicated Victorian Romantic analogy: science is to religion as adulthood is to childhood, and as the modern scientific-industrial world is to the old world. Those who write, and those who enjoy reading, books like *The Lord of the Rings* are saying they prefer the second in each of these pairs. Stern literary critics may disapprove; but we seem to conspire to encourage children to believe things we half-wish we could still believe ourselves. Is not this why a factory-worker, to whom religion means little, yet sends his immaculately turned-out daughter to Sunday School? To give a child, from the first, a purely scientific education along Gradgrind lines would somehow be inhuman and degrading.[6]

All this has been an analysis of John's, 'It's nice to think so, but ...'. He was very young to say such a thing; but then,

[6] In this connection, see the opening chapters of John Stuart Mill's *Autobiography*. 1873.

awareness of the scientific view of the world extends into early childhood nowadays, so that the problem of science and religion —conceived, as we have seen, in rather Victorian terms—confronts a child very early. John, like most people, was inclined to regard the world of science as somehow more 'real' than the world of imagination; but a thorough-going Romantic would insist that the world of imagination is the real world, and the world of science but a pallid abstraction from it. The most splendid expressions of this point of view in our own literature are to be found in William Blake: for example,

> The Atoms of Democritus
> And Newton's Particles of Light
> Are sands upon the Red Sea shore,
> Where Israel's tents do shine so bright.

We shall not adequately discuss the problem of science and religion if we do not reckon with the possibility that Blake may be right. The emergence of modern science-based industrial civilization is, for good or ill, the greatest single upheaval in recorded history. We began, in miniature, with two young children trying to puzzle out its meaning, but we quickly begin to see its immense ramifications.

What of my own contribution to the debate? I suggested that the Creation-story and the evolution-story might both be true. How then are they related?

One answer goes like this. Suppose we ask, *Who threw Sherlock Holmes over the Reichenbach Falls?* Two answers, of different kinds, may be given. One is that, in the story, the Napoleon of crime, Moriarty, dragged Holmes down with him as the two were locked in mortal combat. The other answer is that Arthur Conan Doyle, bored with Holmes, had made it clear that he intended to kill off the great detective: so he wrote the story which ends with the master-sleuth and his foe plunging to their ends together. So, the two statements,

(A) *God made us*, and

(B) *The evolutionary process brought us into being*,

are related to each other in much the same way as,

(A¹) *Conan Doyle killed Holmes*, and

(B¹) *Moriarty killed Holmes*.

7

The essential distinction is between two types of causality. Conan Doyle is the cause of the whole story and everything that happens in it. Everything in the story happens as Doyle intends it to happen. But within the story there is an order of second causes, according to which the plot unfolds, and the characters behave intelligibly. Similarly (it is argued) God is the First Cause of the world (A), but within the world he creates there is an order of second causes (B) which can be investigated without explicit reference to the Author, just as one could write a study of Holmes without having to mention Doyle.

The relation between (A) and (B) is not quite *identical* with the relation between (A^1) and (B^1), because both (A^1) and (B^1) are part of the created order. (A) describes the unique relationship of creation, and though we often speak of a novelist as 'creating' his characters, clearly he does not literally create them as God creates us. God is the one and only-possible First Cause, whereas (B), (A^1) and (B^1) are all instances of secondary causality. Accordingly $R(A^1/B^1)$, i.e. the relation between A^1 and B^1, cannot be *just* the same as $R(A/B)$. But $R(A^1/B^1)$ can be used as an *analogy*, or explanatory *model*, to suggest what $R(A/B)$ may be like. Analogy proper is said by Christian theologians to be a relation between relations. In this particular case, what we are saying is that the analogy helps to show how two quite different kinds of explanation may both be true. Holmes is killed, within the story, by Moriarty; but in a more fundamental sense he is killed off by Conan Doyle. Similarly, in the order of second causes, the evolutionary process has brought the human race into being; but in a more fundamental sense, God is the creator of the whole story in which the evolutionary process is just a part of the plot. The story God is writing is unfinished. He is still creating it. So the analogy suggests that Creation is not something God did a long time ago, but something that is happening in the present moment. To be more exact, God is held to be not temporal at all, but eternal; so the relation of Creation at God's end is rooted in eternity, and at our end sets up the temporal world and governs all that happens in it.

The analogy here is one that has often struck writers. Agatha Christie, in *The Murder of Roger Ackroyd* (1926), made the first-person narrator of the story turn out in the end to be the murderer, so that she could pen the words, 'I am the murderer', in senses (A¹) and (B¹) at once. I wonder if she was making a theological joke to amuse the Bishops, who are well known to be enthusiastic readers of detective stories? In Christian thought the analogy with the author's relation to his characters may be taken still further: for example, it may be said that Jesus, as God Incarnate, is related to God as the first-person narrator within the novel is related to the novelist.

My reply to John, then, amounted to a suggestion that God is the absolute originator of the entire scheme of things, the author of the whole story, and the evolutionary process is part of the plot he writes. This suggests that scientific and religious explanations are logically distinct, and perhaps even that *whatever* events are found to occur, or theories are framed, within the created order, the universal fact of the whole created order's dependence upon God *cannot* be affected. The 'vertical' relationship of everything to its creator is logically independent of our picture of how things go in the 'horizontal' order of second causes.

This view of Creation (and so of the relation of Religion to Science) is that of the modern followers of Thomas Aquinas. It is noticeably a little different from that which the children were considering. They did not ask *Who makes us?*, seeking a timeless cause of the world's origination from moment to moment. The neo-Thomist account of Creation understands 'In the beginning' in an almost wholly non-temporal sense: the eternal God is always originating the world, in every moment that it endures. Caroline, however, like all the myth-makers, put Creation into a special sort of past tense which I called 'mythic time'. The classical discussion of Creation is Augustine's *Confessions*, Books 11–13. Augustine[7] insists that God is eternal, that he does not create in time, that there is no absolute time, and that the time-order is internal to the unfolding created world; yet he nevertheless always speaks of Creation in the *past* tense, in a way for which I believe 'mythic time' is the best phrase.

Now my suggestion to John was that the (A)-order, theological explanation, is of a different kind from the (B)-order, the field

[7] Augustine of Hippo (354–430) was the greatest Christian thinker before Aquinas.

of scientific explanation, and that therefore (A) and (B) cannot be incompatible, and can always both be consistently affirmed. But I have already admitted that this explanation is shallow. It is, I suppose, conceivable that every single thing and event in the world is in a uniform and unique relationship to an extra-cosmic Being. But what is the use of such an idea? Such a First Cause cannot explain anything, or inspire us to do anything; it is morally and intellectually redundant. It reminds one of the game children sometimes play of adding a nonsense-syllable on to the end of every single word, and keeping it up until every adult within earshot is in a fury. A nonsense-noise added uniformly all the time without any intermission cannot *be* a word; it cannot do a job.

Let us pursue the analogy again. Popular complaints, and the need for money, compel Doyle to revive Holmes. So Holmes escapes from the Falls, and returns to tell Watson how he avoided a watery grave, and the clutches of the arch-fiend Moriarty, after all. From Holmes' point of view, within the story, his survival is miraculous. Perhaps a pious friend suggests that the author of Holmes' days has some great work yet for him to do (such as earn more royalties). At any rate, if we are plausibly to imagine the characters within the story thinking about their own author, something pretty striking must happen. Within the (B^1) order there has to be some (A^1) indication of the purposes of the author. Correspondingly, (A)-type explanation is as redundant and remote as the gods of the Epicureans unless there is *some* connection between it and the way we understand, or the way we believe we should act in, the (B) order. We cannot wholly separate (A)-type theological explanation from (B)-type scientific explanation.

Darwin himself gives a good example of this point. After the *Origin of Species* was published some scientists, like Asa Gray, wrote to Darwin saying that they thought his theory compatible with belief in God.[8] Darwin was very cool about this idea, for various reasons, some good, some bad. He doubted if the human

[8] See F. Darwin, *The Life and Letters of Charles Darwin*. London, John Murray 1887. The best and most rigorous single book on Darwin's thought is M. T. Ghiselin, *The Triumph of the Darwinian Method*. Univ. of California 1969.

mind, which was itself a product of biological needs, was competent to deal with such questions. He thought the processes of nature, as he had learnt to see them, were too bizarre, too wasteful and too harsh to be readily viewed as the work of a good God who wills the happiness of his sentient creatures. Could we regard God as having built into the initial endowment of wild dogs or pigeons all the strange varieties subsequently elicited by breeders? What about predation, parasitism and so on? In my novel-analogy, Sherlock Holmes is only a fiction, and there is no moral objection to killing him off, but the bloodstained pages of God's book are filled with the sufferings of real creatures.

But Darwin's chief and best point was this: he had contrasted the artificial selection, by which a breeder of animals develops a new strain, with the process of selection which occurs in wild nature. Many people took this to mean that as a purposing selector is needed in the former case, so he is also needed in the latter. Artificial selection is selection by men for human purposes, natural selection is selection by God for *his* purposes. In this way evolution might be seen as an expression of God's providence, all wild nature be seen as a global farm managed by God, and the argument from design in nature to God as designer be reinstated. But Darwin's real meaning was the opposite of this. His point was that in nature there is *no* purposive selector, no one watching over the animals and picking out those he needs to breed from. If I turn an animal off my farm, I am not handing it over to God's farm, I am leaving it to fend for itself. Wild nature is not like a farm; and natural selection is selection, not by an external selector, but only by the luck of the draw and the harsh struggle for survival. Organisms survive, not because they catch the eye of a cosmic stock-breeder, but because (as the fact of their survival shows) they happen to have the qualities that fit them for survival. What is more, detailed functional analysis of the bodies of organisms at every point shows, not special design for a function, but *improvisation* for a function under the pressure of the struggle for existence.

So Darwin was well aware that his concept of Natural Selection was very different from the old Argument from Design, and he could see that it was strongly resistant to combination with belief

11

in God. In recent years Jacques Monod, in his book *Chance and Necessity* (1970, English translation 1972), has made a similar point, with the advantage of a knowledge of genetics and molecular biology that goes far beyond Darwin's. For Monod the mechanism of evolution, as now understood, rules out any claim that there are final causes, or purposes being realized, in nature. And this, he says, disposes of any philosophy or religion (including both Christianity and Marxism) that believes in cosmic progress or purpose.[9]

Let us now relate this to our earlier argument. In spelling out my composite suggestion that God made us bit-by-bit by evolution, I distinguished,

(A) *God made us*, and

(B) *The evolutionary process brought us into being.*

The claim at first was that (A), the theological claim that God is the First Cause of all things, was a judgement of a quite different kind from (B), the scientific story told about the order of second causes in the world. There is therefore no conflict between science and religion, because they are not in the same business at all.

At the next stage we admitted that the way things go in the world must have *some* bearing on the way God is conceived, on whether we have any reason to believe in him at all, and on whether he is of any importance to us. We only have the (B) story from which to gain any idea as to God's nature and purposes.

But Darwin says cautiously, and Monod says categorically, that, at any rate so far as the process of evolution is concerned, the (B) story is such that it is *not* compatible with belief in God and cannot give us any idea as to God's nature and purposes.

That completes my explanation of why my assertion that God made us bit-by-bit, by evolution, was rather shallow. The question is in fact a great deal more difficult than I admitted. The way things go within the story must affect the ability of the characters to postulate an author of the story, and their picture of his nature and purposes. (It is true that they will think him only if he so writes the story as to lead them to think him, but the question of determinism or predestination is not relevant at the

[9] Monod's views are discussed in Chapter 7, below.

12

moment,[10] because the author can make the characters think him with artistic plausibility only if he so constructs their world as to make it prompt them to think him. So whether they are determined or free does not affect the requirement that there be some trace of the author within the story.) And it is not enough to say that the 'vertical' relationship of creation is different in kind from the 'horizontal' order of events in the story, so that the Creator's authorship is independent of how in detail the story goes. If that be said, the compatibility of religion and science has been purchased at too high a price, the acceptance of a deistic[11] picture of God's relation to the world. But if, recognizing this point, we admit that some traces of God's handiwork must be detected within the story, then we encounter the difficulties to which Darwin draws attention.

DISCUSSION QUESTIONS

Why do we read fairy-tales to children, and not encyclopaedias? What is the function of the world of magic, myth and make-believe?

Why, in some religions, has it been thought so essential to be able to identify points of contact (miracles, answers to prayer, etc.) between God and the world? Are these 'special interventions' necessary to faith?

'New every morning is the love/Our wakening and uprising prove' (John Keble). *Prove?*

---

[10] It is dealt with in Chapter 5, below.

[11] The Deists, English writers of Newton's day, accepted divine Creation, but denied any special revelation or intervention by God in the world. Their God was everything in general, but nothing in particular; and so they fell in the end into atheism.

2

THE LONG BATTLE

We have not yet finished with the debate that was going on in our last chapter, not by any means, but for the moment we need to pause and notice something rather odd about it: something whose oddity we usually overlook, but which becomes very obvious when we step outside our customary assumptions. It is this: why on earth should a technical question about biological theory ever become a matter of specifically religious anxiety at all? Everyone knows religions are very various, but they commonly say something like this: that there is one supremely valuable goal of life or state of being towards which we ought to direct our lives if we wish to attain supreme happiness; that in the teachings of a certain Master, as codified by his followers, there is laid down the Way to attain the goal; that this Supreme Good lies beyond the world of sense; and that by a common effort of shared ritual and prayer and moral endeavour we can together tread the Way and attain the goal. Something like that, surely, is what the religions say; and what has biological theory got to do with it?

If we begin by asking what evolutionary theory looks like from the point of view of Indian religions, and then what it looks like from the point of view of Near-Eastern religions such as Islam and Judaism, we may gain a clearer view of Christianity's peculiar features, which have made the science-religion issue so important in the West.

Certainly Darwinism, when it became known in India, did not startle people as it did in the West, for a variety of reasons. In Indian thought (which is of course at least as diverse as the European tradition) mind and matter are generally not so clearly distinguished as they have usually been in the modern West.[1]

[1] In medieval Europe the distinctions were blurred, and rocks could be regarded as living, stars as animate, and so on.

14

The mental states, the thoughts and feelings of the empirical self are often understood as subtle modifications of the same basic material that underlies everything else in the universe. The line between men and animals is not so clear-cut, either, for both are bound together on the wheel of rebirth. There was no reason for insisting that I am or have a soul in a way that makes me a radically different being from the fly on my nose, when it may turn out that in the next life it and I will find we have changed places. Men, animals, physical nature, and even gods, are all bound up together. It is possible for animals such as cows, monkeys or elephants to be highly venerated, even above holy men, and it is possible for holy men to be ranked even above gods, as they are by the Jains.[2] The Jains' long tradition of non-violence (*ahimsā*) towards all living beings also pointed in the same direction.

Western thought tends to make sharp distinctions between different ranks in creation, and divides God from the world, mind from matter, men from animals, living things from non-living things. These distinctions were the basis of our cosmography (our world-picture), and survive in the classification of subjects in our schools and colleges. The making of these clear distinctions seemed to be of great religious importance, so that a challenge to them seemed to threaten the proper order of creation.

But in India (and of course I am talking about India, and the countries influenced by her, prior to the process of Westernization) people simply did not see it in these terms. To the West it seems religiously important to affirm a special status of man in creation, and something unique about human personality. So to Westerners it seems surprising that the No-self (*an-ātman*, or *anattā*) doctrine should be so common among Buddhists. According to this view, a person is a chain of psychophysical states, like a string of beads with the string removed. If there is an eternal soul in man, as many Indian systems suppose, it is not at all the same thing as the subject of our empirical personal

[2] Jainism, one of India's oldest religions, was founded by Mahāvīra (599–527 B.C.). The Jains pursue sanctity by asceticism, non-violence and compassion to all living things, and are gifted in art and doctrinal speculation.

biography, and in Buddhism the concept of it may be almost wholly refined away. The Buddhist does not have quite the same interest as Westerners have in 'saving his soul', by securing the immortality of an individual personal self.

So for many reasons Darwinism did not cause a great shock in India. If it was saying that men and animals are akin to each other and that there is little qualitative difference between them, then India has always known that. If it was saying that there is no revelation of the workings of the Absolute God in the world of sense, again, India knew that. The supreme goal of religious life was not to be sought within the world of sense anyway. The eternal soul does not belong to the world of sense. The world of sense is beautiful, but it is not as such an expression or manifestation of the goal. The Westerner seeks to discern in the world of sense a God-established order of things (the orders of creation, the natural moral law, the fixity of species), traces of God's developing purposes, signs of his handiwork, and instances of his special intervention. The Asian did not seek these things. He was a superb landscape painter, but there was nothing theological in the way he looked at landscape. He did not, for example, see it as an image of the paradise men had lost by sin, but might yet through grace regain. He just saw it as fleeting and lovely—and turned away from its transience to the eternal concerns of religion. Darwinism would not confute, if anything it would rather *confirm* him in his views.

The flexibility of outlook which a very other-worldly religion may give is best of all illustrated by Buddhism. With its subtle and severely practical spirituality, Buddhism has readily nourished in its monasteries philosophical schools which, from the Western point of view, seem quite incompatible with any sort of religious belief. Buddhism seems able, without doctrinal anxiety, to hold together a variety of philosophical maps of the world.

Again, in the West the arrival of Darwinism challenged traditional notions about beginnings, and about time. Most Westerners reckon that the question of cosmogony (how the world first came to be) is a religious question. A religion ought to include a creation-story, because wonder about why we are here and how it all began is a basic source of religious belief. But in the nine-

16

teenth century physical cosmology, geology and biology were beginning to produce a scientific, non-religious cosmogony. The process by which the cosmos assumed its present structure could be described in a non-theological story. And this scientific cosmogony, even in its rather fragmentary nineteenth-century form, was immediately perceived as a threat to religious belief. Cosmogony was thought to be so centrally a religious topic that the displacement of a religious cosmogony by a historical-scientific cosmogony portended the replacement of religion by science *tout court*. And, after all, this is largely what has happened in the modern West. So it is striking to notice that in India cosmogony is not so important. Few Indian belief-systems have a prominent creation-story of the sort that we have inherited. The Jains, for example, have an elaborate religious cosmography which they express in beautiful diagrams. The cosmos is seen as like a human body. They are intensely religious, on any meaning of the word, and yet they regard the world as eternal and have no idea of creation. The question about the contingency of the world (its might-not-have-been-ness), and its first creation simply does not arise for them, even though they have a highly speculative religious world-picture.

The time-scale question looks different from the Indian viewpoint, too. In the West we contrast the modest time-scale of religion (the world being about 6000 years old) with the vast time-scale of science (the world being now regarded as about 1.6×10^{10} years old[3]). The cosmos of traditional religion seems small, comfortable and highly-wrought. The cosmos of modern science seems vast, awesome, impersonal and indifferent. In India it is, if anything, the other way round. The religious world-pictures are of boundless vastness, whereas the scientific world-picture seems relatively small. One should not take the numbers too literally, but here is one example: Nāgārjuna, a Buddhist writer of *c.* A.D. 100, writing a big commentary on the *Perfection of Wisdom*, describes one view of how long it took Shākyamuni, the historical Buddha, to attain Buddhahood. The transition from being an ordinary man to being a Bodhisattva, who is sure of eventual Buddhahood, took him (because of his extraordinary merits)

[3] That being the period in which, at the present rate of expansion, the cosmos will double in size.

17

only 91 aeons. An aeon is 'a number greater than 10^{28} years'.[4]

As I say, the numbers should not be taken too seriously, but at least it is clear that the religious impact of the new scientific world-view's time-scale cannot be the same in India as it was in the West. In fact to an Indian it could as well seem that Western religion and science have both of them a rather *similar* view of the temporal process as finite, linear and progressive. In comparison with the measureless swirling and revolving aeons of Indian thought, the scientific story—as modern science now tells it—still appears rather Jewish. It is finite, and moves forward step by step, giving something like a cosmic foundation to the Jewish-Marxist ideology of historical development. And that reminds us that to some thinkers the scientific world-picture has seemed itself to be a kind of non-theistic religious myth.[5] I think an Indian philosopher might well judge it to be such, in which case the conflict between religion and science in the West would have to be viewed rather as a conflict between two religions.

To turn now to the Middle East is to turn to more familiar territory, but even here we must proceed with caution. You might think that a conservative Jew, who venerates the Torah (the five Books of Moses, regarded as the source of Jewish religious law) would feel the same difficulty about reconciling the opening chapters of Genesis with modern science as many Christians have felt. But in practice this is not so, for Genesis is not the same kind of book to a Jew as it is to a Christian. To the Jew loyalty to the community and its sacred law counts for more than precise doctrinal definition; and Judaism, with its long traditions of speculative elaboration of the sacred text, allegorical exegesis, and philosophical thought, tolerates a surprising diversity of opinion on matters of doctrine. Within the tradition respected authorities have taught Creation *ex nihilo* (not-out-of-anything, as in orthodox Christianity since early times), *and* Creation out of formless matter; Creation in time,

[4] E. Conze, *Buddhist Scriptures* (Penguin 1959), pp. 30-33. See also Carmen Blacker and Michael Loewe eds., *Ancient Cosmologies* (London, Allen and Unwin 1975), chap. 5.

[5] E.g., Stephen Toulmin, 'Contemporary Scientific Mythology', in *Metaphysical Beliefs,* ed., Alisdair MacIntyre. London, S.C.M. Press 1957.

and the eternity of the world; the pre-existence of the human soul *and* the doctrine that a man is just his body, temporarily animated by God; and so on. Because the Jews are not so credal, not so insistent on doctrinal uniformity, as Christians (for whom doctrine is, much more than for Jews, the basis of community), words like 'conservative' and 'liberal' have a somewhat different meaning in the Jewish context. In its classic heyday Christianity was a whole civilization, an *imperium* and a *universitas*, a vast framework of belief binding together a mixture of peoples and cultures. It aimed, because it had to aim, at a kind of cosmic systematic completeness. The Jews have not been like that. What has mattered to them has been the Word; and the history, the endurance and the destiny of their own people. A Jew's faith is more likely to be put under strain by the historical sufferings and conflicts of his people than by the mechanism of evolution.

Islam is different again. It is an entire civilization, but one more unified than Christianity, less willing to distinguish sacred from profane realms in life, and therefore less willing to allow the emergence and development of secular branches of know-ledge. The best-known writer on our subject it has today is Said Husain Nasr, Persian scholar and historian of Islamic science. Professor Nasr robustly rejects orthodox Darwinism, calling the evidence for it insufficient, and regarding it as in-compatible with the Qur'anic view of God and nature. Thus, in the *Sura* called 'The Bee', God has made mountains and rivers and cattle for the use of man; and he has made man his viceroy, or *khalīfā*, on earth, in a way that resembles traditional Christian accounts of the same theme.[6] The Muslim view of the Qur'ān's authority is as strong, at least as strong, as that taken by strict Christians of the Bible's authority until the early nineteenth century; and Nasr is perhaps more honest than liberal Christians in forthrightly recognizing the incompatibility and concluding that, since Darwin and the Prophet cannot both be right, one at least must be wrong. But the Prophet is right; and therefore Darwin is wrong.

Here at last we seem to be back on more familiar ground! It is clear, I think, that there is no standard, cross-cultural problem of science and religion. The problem takes different

[6] See *Sura* 2, 'The Cow': only Eblis (Satan) refuses to 'worship' Adam.

forms in different cultures; though, with reference to the particular case just discussed, we may guess that the very rapid spread of Western-style university education in the Muslim world will surely lead to conflicts within Islam, paralleling in many respects those that have been experienced in Christian countries.

After this survey we can now recognize one or two of Christianity's peculiar features:

(i) For good or ill, it was in Christian Europe that modern science was born. Highly-developed bodies of scientific knowledge did exist in other cultures (ancient Greece, China, medieval Islam) but only in Europe did a unique take-off into sustained and seemingly unstoppable growth occur. Why this happened, and what the meaning of it is, no one knows. There are a great many theories in the field, but not as yet much agreement. At any rate, it did happen.

(ii) Christianity has always tried to hold disparate peoples and cultures together by doctrine. Being monotheistic, and salvationist, it believes that man is basically capable of attaining to absolute knowledge of a single final truth. It was not race or nationality that bound Christians together, but doctrine. But the great doctrinal syntheses were never quite totalitarian and all-embracing, for Christianity has always harboured, from classical antiquity, an autonomous secular realm.[7] In a curious way Christianity seems to *need* a secular State to contrast with the Church, secular life and natural virtues to contrast with the religious life and the theological virtues, secular love and knowledge to contrast with its own sacred love and sacred knowledge. As a woman needs a husband to cherish, to improve and to rail against, so the Church needs a secular tradition (if I may be forgiven the comparison!). The secular spouse with which Christianity has been in this curious love-hate relationship has sometimes been classical philosophy, sometimes the Emperor, sometimes the men of letters, and, more recently, the men of science. Christianity just happens to be like that.

(iii) In consequence there have now been at least four centuries of science-and-religion bickering in the Western tradition. From time to time it is declared that the quarrel is over, or has been

[7] It was perhaps for this reason that the anatomical dissection of corpses did begin in Christendom, but was not allowed to begin in Islam.

based on a misunderstanding, but all such announcements have turned out to be premature. One of the main themes of this book will be that the quarrel has in fact been highly fruitful and productive; the underlying marriage is at least as important as the superficial squabbling.

But now there is still a further complication. Religions are, after all, very diverse internally. If we study the development of modern Western science, we encounter in the books a portrait of the medieval world-picture which was gradually overthrown during the sixteenth and seventeenth centuries. It is the cosmological and historical framework which Western Christianity had gradually put together out of Plato and Aristotle, the pseudo-Dionysius[8] and Augustine, in an encyclopaedic effort to harmonize into one great system the whole legacy of antiquity. It is the system which underlies Dante and Chaucer, and Milton, its last exponent. It was huge, so big it is hard to know how to begin to describe it. It was based on the Bible and the Creed, from which it took the framework of the creation of the world, the creation of man, the origin of evil, a doctrine of providence, a theology of historical process, the ideas of the incarnation, redemption and the Church, an account of the centuries of grace, leading up to the last judgement, the sealing of hell, the general graduation of the saved from purgatory, and the rejoicings of the blessed in heaven. It was enriched by pagan histories, Aristotle's physics, Ptolemy's ornate geocentric cosmology, and interconnecting patterns of symbolism which ran from one end of creation to the other.

As medieval man stood on the surface of the earth he was conscious of being at the midpoint of creation. As an immortal soul he was the lowest member of the spiritual creation which ranged, rank on rank, above him to the throne of God. As embodied man he was the noblest member of the material creation which ranged, rank on rank, below him. Authority and energy flowed down from above, like the fertilizing rain. The material creation was made of four elements, earth, air, fire and water, which were themselves products of a somewhat precarious

[8] An influential mystical writer of *c*. A.D. 500, who was long mistakenly identified with the Dionysius mentioned in Acts 17.34. His real name is still unknown.

union of the primary qualities, hot, cold, moist and dry. Without the informing energy from above material bodies disintegrate, as man's body does when the soul departs. But this corruptible yet lovely world is of great importance, for it alone changes. The heavenly bodies rotate unchangeably in their crystalline spheres, but here below God has made a world of change. It is going to be a prison for the condemned angels and the damned; but now it is, more importantly, a school in which human souls are being prepared to replenish the depleted ranks of the angels. And that process is history. 'As the spaces above us were filled with daemons, angels, influences and intelligences, so the centuries behind us were filled with shining and ordered figures, with the deeds of Hector and Roland, with the splendours of Charlemagne, Arthur, Priam and Solomon'.[9] History was instructive; it was sacred history. The compilation of the Bible, classical literature, and church history produced an impressively large and on the whole accurate picture of the human past. The human race had begun in the Middle East; the first cities were in Mesopotamia; and thereafter the lineage of civilization ran through Babylon, Persia and Egypt, Greece, the Hellenistic Empires and Rome and on to the history of European Christendom. Everyone felt he stood in that great historical tradition, felt that its heroes were men like himself, and (if he was rich) might employ somebody to trace his own pedigree back through it.

Medieval Christianity had, then, an enormously detailed and complex cosmological and historical world-picture, which only slowly disintegrated between the sixteenth and nineteenth centuries. People struggled to arrest the process of disintegration at almost every step, so that conflict between 'science' and 'religion' could arise over what in retrospect may seem very unlikely issues. An explorer might discover the indigenous inhabitants of the New World; so what was their religious status in terms of Christendom's traditional theology of history? Were they outside the Plan of Salvation? In astronomy, if men were persuaded by the heliocentric model of the solar system, then the great distance the earth travels in six months should produce alterations in the apparent relative positions of the 'fixed' stars. But

[9] C. S. Lewis, *The Discarded Image* (Cambridge 1964), pp. 181f. Still the best single introduction to this subject.

22

no stellar parallax was observable; so it followed that the stars were situated at distances from the earth so vast that the diameter of the earth's orbit was by comparison negligibly small.[10] In a boundlessly vast universe, with perhaps an uncountable number of inhabited worlds (this was already being said by 1600), how could the doings of earthmen, and the story of their Redemption, have the cosmic significance traditionally ascribed to them? Again, in traditional Christian thought, perfection is rest. Everything, from a stone to a soul, seeks a state of rest. Motion is unnatural, rest (or, in the heavens, endless unvarying circular motion) is natural. But here is Galileo proposing a new system according to which motion is the normal state of all things in the universe, and rest is merely a temporary equilibrium of the impelling forces. But if so, says Thomas Hobbes, there can be no Heaven, no actual and unchangeable perfect state of affairs.

Here then is a very striking fact about Christianity: being very monotheistic and very worldly, as well as culturally eclectic, it sought a theologically coherent world-picture on so ambitious a scale that a serious religious difficulty could arise in connection with even such improbable matters as the discovery of a new continent by an explorer, a new theory in astronomy, or a new theory in mechanics. John's and Caroline's argument showed that the old Christian itch to have a comprehensive theological world-picture is still there, so powerfully as to affect even very young children. Who told them that religion in the Christian world is, even in our own secularized days, still such that the mechanism of the origin of animal species is a matter of urgent concern to it? No one told them in so many words. It was one of those deeply embedded things which is communicated unconsciously. I shared their assumption, for I sought to reconcile their respective positions. Our analysis in the last chapter cast doubt on my formula of reconciliation, for we were led to realize that a strict Darwinian view of natural selection is not easy to harmonize with belief in providence. Religion and science are not quite distinct from each other, so that they can sit side by side without quarrel-

[10] This was the main reason why the ancient Greeks rejected the heliocentric theory.

ling; yet is not the very quarrelling an indication that there *could* be a synthesis?

In the present chapter we have learnt that the science/religion issue takes many different forms, for after all, the religions are markedly different from each other in doctrine and in logical character. Christianity's special features are striking. It is a relatively this-worldly religion, it is strongly doctrinal, and as the legatee of the achievement of classical antiquity it developed encyclopaedic ambitions. By the high Middle Ages it had built a majestic synthesis. This only very slowly broke down, through a long series of conflicts over a great variety of issues which have continued right up to the present century. Gradually the various sciences, from astronomy to psychology, established their independence from theology. Once the Queen of the Sciences, whose throne was secure and whose authority, if not unquestioned, could not be disregarded, theology is now—what? A prisoner, in a neglected palace? Or should one rather regard the medieval synthesis as an aberration, and say that Christianity is purer and more vigorous when it is not encumbered with political power and encyclopaedic ambitions? This is the problem of the internal diversity of religion, from which we began this section of our argument. According to your point of view you might (like Matthew Arnold, in 'Dover Beach') see the slow disintegration of the medieval synthesis as a long-drawn-out decline, or you might see it as a process of purification and renewal. It depends upon what view of Christianity you take.

DISCUSSION QUESTIONS

Unlike Christianity, Islam has never admitted an autonomous secular realm of life and thought. In what ways can it respond to the present influx of Western non-religious education, science, technology, and political ideas and institutions?

Consider the meaning of the word 'knowledge', in the phrases 'scientific knowledge', and 'religious knowledge'.

Some philosophers and mystics describe the way to knowledge as a process of unlearning, a journey into unknowing. Why do they do this? Does this suggest that modern religion, stripped-

down and often agnostic, is better than the confident and powerful religion of the Middle Ages?

3

NATURE'S LAW

Jam was being made in the kitchen on a hot day, and the unfortunate cook was battling against squadrons of determined wasps. 'I suppose wasps must have *some* use', she said, 'but for the life of me I can't see what it is.'

It was one of those remarks that sticks in the mind, and I thought about it for long afterwards. It betrayed one of mankind's most ancient and unshakable convictions: that the world is an ordered, interdependent system, in which every created thing has a part to play. Another giveaway is the exclamation, which everyone must have heard at some time or other, 'Why does it have to happen to me? Why just at this moment? What have I done to deserve this?' The world-order is or ought to be just. People on the whole get what they deserve, or do so sufficiently often for us to feel a sense of grievance when we consider life is treating us unfairly.

In such remarks people betray their cosmology—their sense of a cosmic order which is both what the modern jargon calls an 'ecosystem', and a moral order. And every society of men that has ever lived has some ideas, originally religious, about the cosmic order. Nowadays our ideas of the cosmic order are rather fragmented, but if we go back to earlier times we can get a glimpse of their old power and unity.

Take, for example, the ancient Egyptian.[1] He lived along the banks of the Nile, on a narrow plain between barren mountains, which was made highly fertile by the river's annual flood and the hot sun. Egypt was for him the centre of the universe, and the peak of the year was the moment when little hillocks of rich

[1] For a fuller account, see the essay by John A. Wilson in H. Frankfort, ed., *The Intellectual Adventure of Ancient Man*. Chicago 1946, published in Britain as *Before Philosophy*. Pelican 1949.

mud appeared as the flood-waters receded.

To place himself in the world he looked south, to the source of the life-giving waters of the Nile. 'To go south' meant the same as 'to go upstream', and the word for south is also linked with 'face'. The prevailing wind came from the north, 'the back of the head'; so you raised your sail to go south. To the east, 'the left', lay the rising sun, 'God's Land', the place of birth and rebirth. To the west, 'the right', was the setting sun, the place of death and the after-life. Only Egyptians were real human beings; there was a different word for foreigners, who lived in barren hilly places. Since travel was by boat, the sun took his journey across heaven in a boat, and the dead would travel by boat in the underworld.

Having thus 'oriented' himself, the Egyptian framed his idea of the cosmos. The sign for Egypt was ⬤⬤⬤ the flat fertile centre of the earth. The sign for mountain was ⎣⎦ showing the hills on each side of the plain. The sign for foreign country, highland or desert was ⩗⩗

The habitable earth he imagined as a saucer with a corrugated rim—the plain with the mountains on each side—floating in the primeval waters. Heaven was an inverted dish, spangled with stars, and there was a matching counter-heaven for the underworld below. The symbolic centre was the primeval hillock ⌢ 'the place of appearing', which was drawn with the rays of the sun streaming from it; and various temples claimed to be built on this very spot, where the cosmic order was founded. There the sun-god Rē-Atum appeared, and spontaneously generated the pantheon of gods who mark the transition from chaos to cosmos. They take their places—and the world is set in order.

The Egyptian cosmology was, of course, not really so simple as this. They described the world in language which, to our ears, seems full of contradictions, blending physics, mythology and theology, and telling several different stories about everything.[2] Yet there is also a deep unity, in that the State, and religion, and every aspect of social life were cross-linked

[2] For some of the complications, see Veronica Ions, *Egyptian Mythology*. London, Paul Hamlyn 1968.

27

symbolically with, and tied in to, the cosmology. The way the Egyptian saw the world was intensely practical. We often think of mythology and symbolism as products of dreamy, fantastical thinking. Not so. They have the power of binding together different aspects of life which in our day have fallen apart.

A more exalted cosmology is the one developed by the ancient Hebrews, and recorded in Genesis. Its sources are very ancient, and here and there primitive elements stick out, so that one is surprised that the Israelite authors did not eliminate them; God's desire that men shall not gain immortality is an example (3.22), surviving from old Sumerian and Babylonian myths. The creation-story explains how the world began, what its basic structure is, and what is man's place in creation. For the Egyptian, men were just 'the cattle of God'. For the Babylonian, men were serfs: the City is really the creation and habitation of the gods alone, and man's job is merely to sweep out and serve in the vast temples lining the Processional Way. But for the Jew, man is the crown of creation, the climax of God's work.

In the structure of the cosmos we notice two of the same principles as in Egypt. First, to turn chaos into cosmos God must make distinctions. He divides light from darkness, heaven from the primal waters, land from sea, plant from animal, and male from female. Everything is distinguished, and put in its place, so that the various regions of space receive each their proper inhabitants. Similarly, the fundamental rhythms of time are set up (1.14, 8.22). And secondly, there are various levels in the cosmos, which are linked symbolically. Thus the levels move down: cosmos, earth, human race, chosen people, sacred lineage, anointed One. Or again: cosmos, earth, holy Land, holy City, Temple, Ark. Through these different levels the meaning of the cosmos is focused down to a symbolic centre of the earth; a particular spot where God dwells, or a particular man in whom his purpose is concentrated. This is the Jewish equivalent of the Egyptian's primeval hillock, but it is noticeable that for the Jew the most important focus of all is the sacred lineage, the genealogy that runs through Noah, Abraham, Jacob, David and on to the Messiah. History has cosmic significance for the Jew in a way it had not for the Egyptian. It is linear, and moves towards a consummation in the future.

28

A man who lived at about the time when the Genesis stories were taking their final shape was the early Greek philosopher, Thales of Miletus, who lived in the sixth century B.C., and who is traditionally the father of science, the first natural philosopher. No book by Thales is known, and we have to glean what we can from some thirty fragments, anecdotes and quotations, that have been collected from later writers.[3]

Thales was a new sort of man, a *bourgeois*. He was not himself a king, or a priest, or a harassed official, or a worn-out peasant. He was not tied closely to an established sacred order. A typical Greek, he travelled, and was commercially-minded and inquisitive. He was not well-to-do, but he proved that a philosopher can make a living if he puts his mind to it. For, having predicted a heavy harvest well in advance, Thales raised capital, paid deposits on all the olive-presses he could lay hands on, and hired them out during the season at a large profit! But whatever you may wish to say against the *bourgeoisie*, they do produce independent thinkers. Thales gazed at the stars as he walked and fell down a well, making a serving-girl laugh; but he was a very good engineer, astronomer and mathematician. Traditions of his inventions and discoveries have survived.

For his cosmology we are largely dependent on two passages in Aristotle. In one, Aristotle reports that Thales held that the earth stays in place by floating, like a log on water. According to a tradition preserved by Seneca, he further argued that earthquakes occur when the water's movement rocks the earth.

In the other passage Aristotle reports that Thales was the founder of a line of philosophers who sought the first material principle (*archē*) of things, and himself had found it in water. It is not quite clear what is meant by this, but water is a substance which men observe to exist in a variety of forms, solid, liquid and gaseous, which is necessary to life, and which because of its instability is often seen as a symbol of the primal chaos.

Now what strikes us about Thales is the fact that he is half-way between the ancient Egyptian and the modern scientist. There are obviously ancient mythological elements in his thinking:

[3] See G. S. Kirk and J. E. Raven, *The PreSocratic Philosophers* (Cambridge 1957), pp. 74-98.

the earth is still flat, floating on water, and everything comes to be from the primal waters. And after all, he had visited Egypt. Yet he is modern in that his cosmology is not mythological, practical and political, as the Egyptian one was. He is beginning to use explanatory *models*: the earth floats *like* a log on water, earthquakes are *like* the rocking of a floating object. His disinterested curiosity, as he measures pyramids, gazes at the stars or predicts an eclipse, sounds modern. Thales links two ways of thinking, the old and the new, but above all, he and his like are the pioneers of non-religious cosmology. There is a possibility here that in time men's account of the world-order will become dissociated from their account of the social and moral order. Religion had always bound the two together. Now we sense they *could* fall apart.

But this did not happen quickly, or smoothly. For we find that it has still not happened if we leap across twenty-one centuries and consider cosmology on the eve of the scientific revolution—in particular, the account of cosmic law given by Richard Hooker in Book I of *The Laws of Ecclesiastical Polity* (1594). This is a learned, reformed version of the great medieval synthesis, which has survived the Reformation almost intact.

Hooker's vision is of a universe governed by law. A law is 'that which doth assign unto each thing the kind, that which doth moderate the force and power, that which doth appoint the form and measure, of working' (II,1); or more briefly, 'a directive rule unto goodness of operation' (VIII, 4). Everything has an end (a 'final cause') which it seeks, and a proper mode of working in order to attain that end. And the law of each thing bears upon it in the way proper to that kind of thing.

The ultimate foundation of all law lies in the rationality of God, for he alone is a law unto himself. The *First Eternal Law*, then, is that whereby 'the Being of God is a kind of Law to his Working' (II, 2). But God is not only a law unto himself; he is a law to all other things besides. The *Second Eternal Law*, then, is God's will for his creation.

There are three main sorts of creature, and each has its proper kind of law assigned to it. *The Law of Natural Agents* governs all inanimate bodies, which obey it unwittingly. This is what we now call 'the laws of nature'. *The Law of Angels* directs angels

30

to worship God, to organize themselves in a host, and to serve God. *The Law of Men* is the law whereby God orders men towards the perfection he intends for them. Human law is especially complex, because unlike angels and beasts, man needs education and instruction to reach his full potential for rationality and moral goodness. The three main sorts of human law are *The Natural Moral Law*, the basic, rationally-knowable principles of morality; *Laws Politic*, imposed by society exercising its God-given authority; and the *Supernatural Laws* of faith, hope and charity, revealed in Scripture, whereby man can attain holiness.

There are many more subdivisions. For example, *Laws Politic* are divided into civil and ecclesiastical laws; and civil laws are then further subdivided into national and international laws. But that is enough. What is Hooker doing in all this?

In the first place, we realize as we go on that Hooker is giving a cosmological backing to the orderly Mattins and Evensong that are read in an English village church. The vast vision of cosmic order is tied to an *apologia* for the English constitution, and the established Church of England, in much the same way as in ancient Egypt!

Secondly, the cosmology is determined by what we would now call the 'arts' subjects rather than the 'science' subjects. The very *word* 'science' did not get its modern meaning till the early nineteenth century. In Hooker's day we are still in a Renaissance world. The studies that really determine man's place in the universe are humane letters (Latin, Greek and Hebrew), Divinity and Law.

Only a hundred years later, the situation has been utterly transformed. Isaac Newton also portrays a cosmos governed by universal law, but the meaning of the word 'law', and the character of the cosmology, are utterly different. People tried to mask the greatness of the change. For example, Hooker quotes (II,3) *Wisdom of Solomon* ix, 20: 'Thou hast ordered all things in measure and number and weight'; and this same text later became a favourite with the men of the Royal Society, most of them devout Anglicans, as giving scriptural warrant for the new mathematical analysis of nature. But they meant by it something really very different from what Hooker had meant.

31

Robert Boyle[4] once argued from the new laws of nature to a divine lawgiver (in *The Christian Virtuoso*, 1690), but he realized—because he dropped the argument—that material bodies were no longer being thought of as 'obeying' laws in the old theological sense. Newton himself tried to keep together the old literary approach to reality (based especially on Scripture) and the new mathematical approach in Natural Philosophy, but he failed. For a fundamental change *had* taken place, and it could not be denied.

In the first edition of *The Mathematical Principles of Natural Philosophy* (1687) Newton barely mentions theology, in accordance with the Baconian injunction that science (then called philosophy, or natural philosophy) should be kept separate from religion. The Book of Nature was written in numbers, the Book of Scripture was written in words. Newton wrote in a notebook: 'religion and philosophy are to be preserved distinct. We are not to introduce divine revelations into Philosophy, or philosophical opinions into religion'.[5] This says as clearly as can be that the old cosmologies, which bound together the natural order and the social order, are finished. Newton and his disciples were not always consistent in keeping religion and science apart, but the first edition of the *Principles* demonstrated for all time what a purely mathematical approach to cosmology could achieve. Newton lays down a system of mechanics and then demonstrates that the cosmos conforms to it. And the result was not mere 'hypothesis', as Osiander[6] had said of Copernicus, and as papal officials had suggested to Galileo; for the earth's motion had to be real, not relative, or the centrifugal and gravitational forces would not balance. So Copernicus was at last *proved* right about the motion of the earth. Newton had correctly identified one of the fundamental forces in nature, given a correct mathematical

[4] Robert Boyle (1627–91), Father of Chemistry, co-founder of the Royal Society, and Anglican apologist. *The Christian Virtuoso* was one of the first books trying to show that a scientist, or 'virtuoso', could be a good Christian.
[5] Cited in F. E. Manuel, *The Religion of Isaac Newton* (O.U.P. 1974), p. 28.
[6] Osiander (1498–1552), Lutheran theologian, wrote a preface to Copernicus' famous book, suggesting that its theory was just a 'hypothesis', a possible model.

description of it, and so was able to link the planetary orbits, a falling apple, the flight of a projectile and the motion of the tides in a clear and rigorous system of purely mathematical explanation. It was not a question of making observations, framing inductive generalizations, and then revealing a rough conformity to a mathematical pattern; it was a question of laying down a formal mathematical pattern and demonstrating that the world strictly conforms to it. And this showed the power and rigour of applied mathematics as never before.

Newton himself, of course, used the Argument from Design, and God played a part, if somewhat residual, in his natural philosophy. But it is not surprising that, as his achievement was digested, men should conclude that the Book of Nature, written in numbers, was very different in character from the Book of Scripture, the world of moral and religious belief and symbolism; and if it came to an issue between the two, the kind of knowledge which the former yielded was superior to the kind of knowledge which the latter yielded.

There were various ways in which religious men could respond to this situation.

Pietists in Germany, and Methodists in Britain, largely gave up the cosmological side of religious belief. The main emphasis began to move from Creation to Redemption; from finding God at work in the world of nature to finding him at work in the human soul. Religious concepts were applied rather less to external events, and rather more to the believer's inner experience. Religion became more a matter of feeling, more 'evangelical', and more sectarian. This line of development, a process of internalization, continued over a very long period, until it was challenged, quite recently, by the progressive extension of the scientific method and outlook to man and his 'inner' life. A late and unorthodox example of internalization at its furthest extreme is the Swiss psychologist C. G. Jung (1875–1961), the son of a Protestant pastor. In his later years Jung was deeply concerned with religion, but for him it exists *solely* in the realm of psychological or subjective truth. Since most people nowadays take a rather subjective view of religious truth, it is often not noticed how extreme Jung is. But if we set beside him Thomas Aquinas' *Summa Theologiae, Pars Prima*, the contrast is obvious. Aquinas is majestically calm, objective, cosmological and systematic. He is not self-revelatory; indeed he is simply not interested in the inner life in the modern sense. He knows nothing of the exploration of the self through the novel, drama, and introspection. But if, for Aquinas, the inner world barely exists, for Jung the external world barely exists. It is a reminder of the extraordinary diversity of religion, and the ways in which religious concepts are highly flexible, and capable of many different sorts of application.

Another line of response in the post-Newtonian situation was to claim that the Newtonian cosmos was still 'Creation', discernibly the work of a good and wise God. It might be argued that the evidence of God's unity and rationality was stronger than ever, now that Newton had demonstrated the conformity of the world to universal mathematical laws. If it were said that for all we know matter, motion and number were eternal and need no creator, it could be replied that the universe still exhibited not only mathematical order, but benevolent contrivance, especially in the plant and animal kingdoms. The argument about natural theology and natural religion, which went on throughout the eighteenth century and for some while afterwards, was at bottom an argument about whether the Newtonian cosmos could still function in the ways in which earlier cosmologies had functioned, as providing an objective basis for religion and morality. Eventually the argument was largely lost, partly because of the forceful criticisms which philosophers such as Hume and Kant brought against the proof of God from Nature, and partly because in the nineteenth century geology and biology developed their own methods of explanation of many of the phenomena to which the natural theologians had appealed.

Another way for theology to take was to make a clear distinction between the realm of nature and the realm of history. Newton himself had taken such a line. His natural philosophy was non-historical and non-evolutionary. His main emphasis had been on why the world remains a stable system, rather than on how it has reached its present state. In religion, on the other hand, Newton was strongly historically-minded, rejecting mystical and philosophical kinds of religion in favour of religion based on history, society and morality—biblical religion, in fact. Like many who followed, he tried to keep together mathematical cosmology and sacred history.

But we should notice a few of the implications of doing this. In the first place there are two kinds of time. In natural philosophy (Scholium to the Definitions, *Principles*, Book I) time is thus defined: 'Absolute true and mathematical time, of itself and from its own nature, flows equably without relation to anything external, and by another name is called "duration"; relative, apparent and common time is some sensible and external (whether accurate or unequable) measure of duration by the means of motion, which is commonly used instead of true time, such as an hour, a day, a month, a year'.

But in sacred history we are working with a very different idea of time. Newton fully believed that God intervened, and frequently so, in the cosmos he had created. In fact Leibniz complained[7] that there must be something wrong with a cosmos into which so many incursions had to be made. Nevertheless, Newton believed in them, and in a way saw the whole of human history as a vast divine intervention. For he regarded all history as the progressive unfolding of a divine plan, with successive epochs, differentiated from each other theologically. He loved to draw maps of universal history based on his exegesis of Daniel and Revelation. So Newton saw the time order within which sacred history unfolds in a strongly theological (and even mythological) way, which is notably different from the mathematical ideas of time he employs in natural philosophy.

But nature and history cannot be kept quite distinct, and it was inevitable that much attention should be given to *miracles*, as historical 'evidences of Revelation', in the eighteenth century.

Miracles had not been such a problem in prescientific thought. Since God upheld the whole natural order, directing everything in its proper course, and since everything in nature was a manifestation of his power, his miraculous action was only an intensified form of his regular action. Miracles rather confirmed than overthrew one's ordinary picture of the natural order in its de-

[7] H. G. Alexander, ed., *The Leibniz-Clarke Correspondence*. Manchester University Press 1956. For Leibniz' ideas about God, see Chapter 5, below.

pendence on the power of God, so that we often find them reported in an oddly matter-of-fact way.

Newton's belief in God's power and sovereignty was very strong, and he saw no difficulty in reconciling, under God, an exalted picture of cosmic order in natural philosophy with continual interventions in that order; some in nature, but far more in history, as God intervened to reveal his will, to restore true religion, and to put right things that were going wrong.

However, in spite of Newton himself, the concept of history was steadily secularized in the eighteenth century, and the concept of miracle began to crack under the strain that was being placed upon it. The story shows an odd paradox in the idea of miracle. For, to be able to identify a miracle as such, you have to contrast it with the normal course of events against which it stands out as an exception. So the stronger your sense of the regular course of nature becomes, the more vividly the miraculous exception stands out. Accordingly, many Christian apologists emphasized (i) the regularity of nature, (ii) the extraordinariness of such a miracle as the Resurrection, and (iii) the great reliability of the testimony of the Apostles to it. The more strongly they could emphasize *all three* of these factors, the more conclusive the proof of the truth of Christianity would appear. But eventually miracles became so extraordinary as to be incredible, and this is the point reached in David Hume's famous essay on miracles, first published as Chapter X of *An Enquiry Concerning Human Understanding* (1748). The best example of what Hume was overthrowing is Thomas Sherlock's *The Tryal of the Witnesses of the Resurrection of Jesus* (1729).

From a purely philosophical point of view, there are faults in Hume's argument. But if we look at his chapter in its historical context, we can see better what he means and why he is right. What has happened is that two lines of thought have crossed each other. Hume deals with them in separate parts of his essay.

The first is that, as men's sense of the natural order has grown stronger, apologists have made more and more of the extraordinariness of miracles, to the point at which the very notion of a miracle begins to break up: 'A miracle is a violation of the laws of nature; and as a firm and unalterable experience has established those laws, the proof against a miracle, from the very nature of the fact, is as entire as any argument from experience can possibly be imagined.'

The other point is that, as standards of historical criticism rise, the historical testimony to miracles begins to look vulnerable: 'No testimony for any kind of miracle has ever amounted to a probability, much less to a proof; and ... even supposing it amounted to a proof, it would be opposed by another proof, derived from the very nature of the fact, which it would endeavour to establish.' Hume concludes that the apologists had overplayed their hand: 'a miracle can never be proved, so as to be the foundation of a system of religion'.[8] The rising extraordinariness of miracles has passed the falling credulity of historians, and the argument from miracle has blown up in the apologists' faces.

As I say, there are faults in Hume's argument: notice the question-begging word 'unalterable' above, for example. But in the main, he is right. What had happened was that the success of the new natural philosophy had forced people towards a very interventionist idea of God's action in the world. But there was real difficulty in identifying those interventions as such, and erecting religious doctrine upon them. The idea was to give a non-theological definition of a miracle (as a violation of the natural order) and a non-theological proof of its occurrence (straightforward historical evidence). Thus established, purely rationally, the miracle would provide an objective anchorage for Revealed Theology in an increasingly irreligious universe.

Most theologians now regard this line of apologetics as having been mistaken. The late Professor C. A. Coulson (an Oxford mathematician and Methodist layman) coined a famous phrase which sums up much of what was wrong with it: 'the God of the gaps'. The idea is that as scientific ways of explaining the world became more powerful and comprehensive, the scope for theological explanations of events contracted. God was left filling the gaps in the scientific world-picture. But these gaps are liable to be closed. Newton still invoked God to correct the planetary inequalities, and so preserve the stability of the solar system; but the Frenchman Laplace later recalculated all the

[8] These quotations are taken from L. A. Selby-Bigge, ed., *Hume's Enquiries* (O.U.P. many editions), paras. 90, 98, 99.

orbits with better data and mathematical methods and found that he was able, in his famous phrase, to declare, 'I have no need of that hypothesis'. Similarly, Darwin still left to God the creation of the very first living things, but modern molecular biology has been increasingly able to suggest a plausible account of how the first and simplest self-replicating protein molecule could have been formed. A God-of-the-gaps, who acts only in special interventions, is liable to be squeezed out altogether, and is in any case a great deal less than the universal creator of traditional theology.

So the question of the relation between the religious and the scientific world-pictures is still unsolved. Before leaving it we may suggest two lines of thought which may contribute to solving it, and which readers may like to pursue for themselves.

The first is that the scientific world-picture is now much less drastically mechanistic and austere than it used to be. The original idea was to give a total account of the universe in terms of three basic concepts: matter, motion and number. Thoroughgoing determinism suggested that there could be a complete state-description of the universe, and a complete knowledge of all the laws of change, so that from a full description of the universe at any one instant all future states of affairs could be exactly computed. But few now would take such an extreme view. As the branches of science have grown more numerous, and have established each their own distinctive concepts and methods, their picture of the world has grown both more tentative and more rich and various. It is very doubtful whether, for example, the basic concepts of biology can be reduced without remainder to those of physics. The environmental revolution shows the emergence, within the scientific community, of something rather like old religious pictures of an interdependent natural order within which man has a proper place, and which he should respect and be guided by. So it is possible that the gap between religious and scientific ways of seeing the world is closing. There may be a certain convergence taking place, though we must be careful not to beg the question of what the religious outlook of future men may be.

Secondly, and cutting somewhat across the first point, it should be remembered that the great religions of the world do not simply celebrate the cosmos as being already a finished and perfect divine order. They are also religions of redemption or release, which in different ways look beyond the world of sense for the supreme good. So we should not expect them to have a stable religious cosmology in quite the same sense as ancient Egyptians or Babylonians. This present world-order is described as religiously *un*satisfactory; it is seen as fleeting, illusory, imperfect, or corrupted by evil. It must be redeemed, or man must be redeemed from it. And so we should expect there to be *some* tension between science's picture of the world as it is, and religion's vision of the perfect good, the world as it should be. If God were perfectly manifest within the world as it is disclosed by science to be, then there would be no need of redemption or salvation. But the great religions themselves say that the world of empirical fact is not a final and satisfactory home for the human spirit. *Some* tension between religion and science is therefore to be expected.

DISCUSSION QUESTIONS

Is it true that human society can exist only on the basis of some shared vision of the cosmic order?

Can modern Western science provide such a cosmological foundation for social life and morality?

Consider the various meanings and uses of the words 'natural' and 'unnatural', 'higher' and 'lower'.

4

MAN AS A SUBJECT FOR SCIENCE

It is a mistake to suppose that it was only the work of Darwin that forced the recognition that man is part of nature, and as such, part of the proper subject-matter of natural science. On the contrary, one of the few things we can be sure of about the earliest men is that they were preoccupied with the affinities between themselves and animals.[1] In every society the common language connects the stages of life, the behaviour and the anatomy of men with those of animals, and in every society symbolic correspondences between the human realm and the animal realm are recognized. A glance through the Grimms' *Fairy Tales*, or a brief examination of 'totemism' among Amerindians, Australian aboriginals or Rugby football teams,[2] reminds us that virtually every familiar species of animal is drawn on to provide symbols for human groups, and human personality traits and behaviour. Animals are understood in human terms, and humans in animal terms.

But if it has always been recognized that man is part of nature, it has also usually been thought that in some respects man transcends nature, or has a special place in nature. The line between man as part of nature (and so a proper topic for scientific study) and man as transcending nature (especially in his rationality, morality and religion) has been very variously drawn at different times. The drawing of this line is indeed the problem of science and religion in miniature.

For centuries it was the medical profession which, more than any other, bore the brunt of the conflict here, and our deeply

[1] As is shown by the oldest surviving cave-paintings and sculpture. The earliest evidences of ritual are neolithic drawings of men dressed as animals—in particular, stags.

[2] They call themselves lions, wallabies and so on. Compare mascots.

40

ambiguous attitudes towards doctors are relics of those old troubles. They reveal the fears which surrounded the application of the scientific method to man.

Consider, for a moment, the traditional apparatus of horror films. Almost all of it is the residue of old scandals and legends surrounding the figures of the anatomist, the surgeon and the physician. The apparatus is medical or alchemical: the locked laboratory, the bubbling retorts, the fanatical lust for knowledge, premature burial, the exhumation of corpses in graveyards at midnight, mesmerism, operating-table horrors, exotic surgical constructions, and so on. Still more revealing is the psychology imputed to the man of science. His detachment and curiosity are seen as sublimated sadism and as arrogance on the brink of insanity, and his desire for forbidden knowledge and godlike power bring down supernatural retribution on his own head. He topples from near-divinity to gibbering idiocy.[3] Myths of this kind have gathered round a series of figures—Bluebeard and Count Dracula, Faust and Frankenstein, Drs Jekyll and Moreau —and how they still pull in the crowds!

Historically, the primary image of the doctor was this fearsome one. Sir Thomas Browne, the Norwich physician, wrote his *Religio Medici*, 'the religion of a medical man', in about 1635,[4] and he felt obliged to admit the paradox of his title in his very first sentence: 'The general scandal of my profession' and 'the natural course of my studies' might well persuade the world that such a man could have no religion. Doctors were already by repute infidels. Browne was consciously paradoxical in his view of religion, in his insistence that the very anatomical data which made his colleagues sceptical were for him arguments for faith:

In our study of anatomy there is a mass of mysterious philosophy, and such as reduced the very heathens to divinity; yet, amongst all those rare discoveries and curious pieces I find in the fabrick of man, I do not so much content myself, as in that I find not,—that is, no organ or instrument for the rational soul; for in the brain, which we term the seat of reason, there

[3] One of the first English mad scientists, a comic one, is the hero of Thomas Shadwell's play *The Virtuoso* (1676).
[4] Pirated 1642; authorized edition, 1643.

41

is not anything of moment more than I can discover in the crany of a beast: and this is a sensible and not inconsiderable argument of the inorganity of the soul ... (Sect. XXXVI)

The very fact that on the dissecting-table man is indistinguishable from a beast serves only to heighten Browne's feeling for the mysterious contrast between the world of fact and the world of faith.

Yet it is odd that all this should be so. In Browne's day the greatest medical school in Europe had, for 150 years, been the one at Padua, and Padua's greatness was based on the biological works of Aristotle and the medical works of Galen. A line of great anatomists, including Andreas Vesalius (1514-64), author of the *De Fabrica* (1543), Gabriele Fallopio (1523-62), and Fabricius of Acquapendente (1537-1619), successively held the Chair of surgery and anatomy. The great artists of the day took a close interest in their work. Florentine painters made anatomical drawings, and many paintings survive showing the anatomists at work. The ancient text-book is much in evidence, being read as the dissection proceeds. The atmosphere is rather reverential than impious; the conjunction of Renaissance humanism, ancient learning, and anatomical study, shows that men still thought that the meaning of the universe was somehow expressed in miniature in the human body. William Harvey had studied under Fabricius, and Browne himself had studied at Padua, a few years after Fabricius' death. And the Paduan tradition, as exemplified in such men, was strongly conservative. It was not at all in the new sceptical, atomistic or mechanical mode, but still thought in organic and teleological (purposive) ways learnt from Aristotle. Thus, in his great book on the circulation of the blood, *De Motu Cordis et Sanguinis* (1628), Harvey links the motion of the blood with cyclical movements in nature. Circular motion is the most perfect, and the most suitable to man the microcosm, the miniature world.[5]

Old-fashioned histories of science like to depict the Paduan anatomists and their pupils as a line of revolutionaries, but they were not. Only later, after the spread of Descartes' mechanical

[5] See Hugh Kearney, *Science and Change 1500-1700* (London, Weidenfeld and Nicolson, World University Library 1971), pp. 77-88.

view of living bodies, was the human body secularized, or (as the sociologists say) demystified. For Fabricius and Harvey the human body was still as sacred a thing as it had been for Michelangelo himself.

So it is far from clear why Browne should admit that the medical men were notorious for their impiety. Something deeper and less articulated than their overt activities and attitudes seems to be involved, something we can only guess at, in a rather impressionistic way. The human body is in a fundamental sense the first thing we know, and the chief source of the analogies by means of which we understand all else. The line between the human body and the surrounding world is a very important frontier, so that in all cultures anything that ruptures or crosses that frontier is surrounded by ritual. Whether we consider the book of Leviticus, or traditional Hindu rituals, or any other culture, time and again we notice the intense ritualization that surrounds eating, excretion, discharges from the body, hair and nail-clippings, cleanliness, sickness and corpses. Much of religion has been concerned with the preservation of the integrity of the body.[6] And however we draw the line between the provinces of science and religion, the human body is going to straddle that line. Whether we say that science is concerned with the external world, and religion with the inner life; or that science is concerned with fact, and religion with value; or that science is concerned with numbers, and religion with words; or that science is concerned with plain description, and religion with symbolism —however we try to make the distinction, the living human being includes both branches of it, as he eats and drinks, makes moral choices, kicks a stone, works, paints a picture, prays to God, and rots in his grave. Perhaps the reasons for the 'impiety' of medical men are two: first, the intense archaic emotion surrounding the human body; and secondly, that at least since the sixteenth century men have struggled to draw a workable line of demarcation between the provinces of science and religion, but wherever the line has been drawn, the medical man finds himself on it. For very ancient symbolic reasons that line tends to be seen as the surface of the human body, which is why (as anyone who has worked in an operating theatre will testify) the

[6] On these themes see Mary Douglas, *Natural Symbols*. Pelican 1973.

43

most tense moment in a surgical operation is the primary incision.

Because the medical man is on the line, he is seen sometimes as a kind of black magician, and sometimes as a godlike or priestly figure. 'In our time it is the physician who exercises the cure of souls', said Kierkegaard, sardonically, in 1851,[7] the first of a line of critics of the rising status and pretensions of medical men.

But there was also a second line along which the scientific method began to be applied to man, and this line is quite different. It is statistical.

In the sixteenth and seventeenth centuries men were coming more and more to perceive the world through, and in terms of, mathematical grids. The most obvious example is the lines of latitude and longitude laid over the surface of the terrestrial globe by cartographers, as an aid to navigation. Time and space began to be seen in these terms too. For example, the dating of events on a common world-wide time-scale of centuries A.D. and B.C. became gradually more common, though the process was slow, and the first century in which many or most men said to themselves, 'We live in the —th century', was the nineteenth. The crucial step is the changeover from units of measurement closely tied to natural phenomena to purely abstract scales. It is a changeover that has happened very irregularly. Geometry moved in classical antiquity from being closely tied to plumb-lines, levels, shadows cast by sticks, right angles constructed with knotted ropes, and areas of land paced out, to being a purely formal system, whereas measures of length, weight and volume are in English-speaking countries being converted to the more abstract metric system only in our own day. Lawyers, seldom the most progressive of people still date Statutes by the Sovereign's regnal year, and not in A.D. dating!

Nevertheless, the change has gradually been occurring, and the eighteenth century was a time when, under the influence of Newton's success, men were particularly enthusiastic for it. In Georgian architecture and town-planning the grid becomes visible, as it does in those places where progressive landowners transformed irregular fields and winding country lanes into

[7] In W. Lowrie tr., *Judge for Yourselves!* (O.U.P. 1946), p. 210.

rectangular fields and straight lanes.[8] In the most eighteenth-century of all countries, the United States, the grid of fields and streets is in many places startlingly visible from the air today.

But how was mathematical order to be brought into government and human affairs? Most seventeenth-century writers still felt that life is full of uncertainties, that no man knows when death will come, and that it is best to expect the end at any moment. In such a frame of mind it is hard to believe that any calculus can come to grips with the uncertainties of life.

The clue lay in the idea of *probability*, which gradually developed in English thought between Hooker and Butler. Human life is admittedly such that mathematical (or 'metaphysical') certainy, the certainty of necessary truth, is never possible in human affairs. But, said many English moralists, moral certainty —or, as it was later called, 'probable evidence'—is sufficient to act upon. 'Probability is the very guide of life', in Joseph Butler's famous phrase,[9] and it was in England that the application of a probability-calculus to human life developed most quickly (Sweden was the chief rival).

One pioneer was Dr Richard Price, F.R.S. (1723-91), a man of curious and varied talents and historical importance. He was a Unitarian minister; he was a distinguished moral philosopher; he gained his F.R.S. for papers on, in particular, the mathematical expression of probabilities; and finally, in 1771 he published his *Observations on Reversionary Payments*, which began the long labour of setting the infant Life Assurance business on a sound mathematical basis.[10]

[8] See the mathematical grid on a modern tower-block, and notice how modern architecture is closer in spirit to the formalism of eighteenth-century architecture, than to the rich symbolism of nineteenth-century architecture. As the men of the Enlightenment thought Gothic barbarous, so early twentieth-century men thought Victorian barbarous.

[9] From the preface to *Analogy of Religion*. 1736.

[10] Alex Wood, *Thomas Young* (C.U.P. 1954), pp. 297ff., has further details. See also the entry for Price in the Dictionary of National Biography. *Ian Hacking, *The Emergence of Probability* (C.U.P. 1975), gives a full account of the development of the idea of probability. Our special interest is in the changeover from a religious to a mathematical attitude to death. Formerly people thought the changes and chances of this mortal life incalculable by men, but now they begin to be calculated.

* Asterisked books are not recommended for beginners.

The eighteenth century was the first in modern times which had a clear common picture of a long-term earthly future for the human race. In that period, with its zeal for improvement, the classical religious attitude to death ('Watch and pray, for ye know not the hour') was replaced, especially among capitalists, by a calculus of the probability of death, by saving, by prudent provision for the future—in short, by that whole attitude to the future which is epitomized by Life Assurance. It is a kind of secular salvation, which has borrowed the language of Protestantism ('provident', 'assurance', etc.), and which, instead of gaining heaven by good works, gains a blessed retirement by prudent provision.

The taking of a census, regarded by ancient Jews as a sin against God (1 Chron. 21.1), became one of the duties of government, and techniques for measuring various attributes of human populations slowly developed. Only on the basis of such information could the kind of rational social planning now thought desirable be carried on. The civil registration of births and deaths, for example, began in Britain in 1836, and the first modern census took place in 1851.

Yet there has always been opposition, and to this day the question is still hotly debated. Just like primitive men, we feel that to give information about ourselves to another is to some extent to put ourselves in that other's power. Where the other is the State itself, armed with modern methods of storing, processing and retrieving information, our anxiety is fully justified, and there is a good deal of talk nowadays about entrenching a right to privacy in the civil law, perhaps as part of a major Bill of Rights. This would, it is hoped, set permanent limits to the power of the State over the individual.

In this connection, we notice the strongly religious character of the language used in speaking of individual rights. Words like 'inviolable', 'sacred', 'value', 'sanctity' and so on are used in connection with the defence of a region of personal life against the all-knowing state-power. Some aspects of our life are legitimately open to public inspection and subject to legal coercion, but there is a region which ought to remain hidden and inviolate. And as we suppose there to be limits to the State's knowledge of and power over us, so presumably we must correspondingly suppose there are limits to the extent to which the sciences of man can give a complete account of us.

One suspects that many people are not clear at this point whether the claim that they are making is descriptive or ethical. There are at least *three* possible interpretations:

(i) It may be held (on metaphysical or theological grounds) that we must affirm human freedom of thought and action, and the presence in man of an immaterial soul, the core of the self. Thus, though (since we are embodied animal beings) much about us can be measured and is quite properly a subject for science, the core of what makes a human being a person is outside the scope of science, and can neither be completely known by scientific method, nor be entirely subject to the civil power.

(ii) It may be held that, since sociological generalizations are statistical, and the causes of *individual* human behaviour too complex ever to be wholly unravelled, we can have statistical information about the behaviour of large groups of men,[11] without pretending to be able to predict the behaviour of individuals. But governments, and social scientists, are normally interested only in predicting, and legislating for, the behaviour of large groups of men, not of individuals. Thus the individual can always console himself with the thought that he is or may be an exception. To defend the private realm, or the value of the individual, is no more than to point out the merely-statistical character of the generalizations of social science.

(iii) It may be held that no limits can be laid down in advance to the extent to which the sciences of man may be able to give a complete account of us. It is possible that thoroughgoing determinism is true. Nevertheless, on purely ethical grounds we can require the State to limit itself, and to refrain from taking full advantage of the powers which the sciences of man put into its hands. Thus, to give an example, the science of criminology might be brought to such a pitch that it could be predicted 'beyond all reasonable doubt' (that is, with as much certainty as

[11] The terms 'man' and 'men', in their primary sense, include of course both male and female human beings. It is a philolcgical accident that English lacks a 'marked term' for adult male human beings, so that they are called simply 'men'. Many other languages are clearer, but the lack in English causes much confusion.

47

the Courts normally require in order to convict) that a certain individual will shortly commit a serious crime. But even so, on ethical grounds, it might be decided that though the State has this knowledge, it should not be given the right to deprive the individual in question of his liberty until he has actually committed the crime and been duly convicted.

In position (i) civil liberty is defended by the metaphysical claim that *determinism is false* and we are free. In position (ii) it is defended by the claim that, in human affairs at any rate, *determinism is merely statistical*. We may be free as individuals, though predictable in the mass. Position (iii) admits that *determinism may be true*, but the authorities can be obliged for moral reasons to limit the use of their ever-growing power to control our behaviour.

Position (iii) may have the air of a rearguard action in defence of a conception of freedom which we fear may be illusory. But, broadly, the past century *has* seen a shift from a moralistic to a more deterministic view of the individual. Thus alcoholism in the nineteenth century was seen as a *moral* problem, to be remedied by persuasion, by signing the pledge, and by moral support, whereas in the twentieth century it is seen as a *medical* problem, whose causes can be ascertained, and which can be cured by medical techniques. A detailed comparative study of the two different attitudes to alcoholism, and a comparison of their therapeutic effectiveness, would be a fascinating exercise, and it might show a relation between sociology and metaphysics. In a society which *believes* in freedom, men *are* free; and in a society which does *not* believe in freedom, but believes that men's behaviour is causally determined, then men are *not* free. That is to say, metaphysical and religious doctrines are not simply purporting to express timeless and absolute truths about the human condition; they are also proposals for the construction of various social orders. And when we reflect about the extraordinary development of the sciences of man, and the ways in which they are affecting our lives, our thought has a *political dimension*. Knowledge is power, and knowledge about men is power over men. In the case of the sciences of man, who decides, and by what criterion, what kinds of behaviour are socially desirable, and what anti-social? Is it simply religious obfuscation to express anxiety that some of the boldest programmes for a 'technology of behaviour' are implicitly totalitarian?

In connection with position (i) above, the claim that there is a sacred, hidden and inviolable region of the self and of personal life, we notice echoes of an ancient religious symbolism: 'The LORD has set the sun in the heavens, but has said that he would dwell in thick darkness'. All over the world, what is most sacred is not exposed to the light of day, nor is it clearly apprehended; it is veiled and hidden, perhaps, like the sun, by its own very brilliance. The language of sanctity and inviolability, used in connection with the self, private life and marriage, is a Protestant and 'internalized' version of an old religious theme. But the claim need not be put in quite these terms. The philosopher Immanuel Kant was a man of the Enlightenment, implacably hostile to religious obscurantism. But he would have made claim (i). He allowed that the empirical self is part of nature, as such is subject to universal causal law, and therefore is in principle completely knowable by empirical psychology. But Kant also asserted that the self as moral agent transcends nature, and is not empirically knowable. When we engage in pure thought, or resolve to act in accordance with purely *a priori* (that is, independent of the world of experience) principles of morality, we transcend nature. We are timeless. Kant's emphasis on reason and morality, and his individualism, are not expressed in traditional religious symbolism, though he is clearly a product of Protestantism; but he is certainly flatly opposed to any kind of totalitarianism based on a naturalistic view of man.

A third element in the development of the sciences of man which we should notice is the changeover, in the nineteenth century, from Newtonian to Darwinian models.

The older scientific thinking about man was characterized by *elementarism*, and by the idea of a *balance of forces*. Elementarism has a long history. The Paduan mathematicians, and Galileo, believed in a technique of enquiry which they called the method of resolution and composition. To study some topic, it must first be 'resolved', or broken down to its elementary constituents, and then 'composed', or put together again. Such a method fitted well with the rising popularity of atomism in philosophy; and atomism was increasingly becoming not only a metaphysical doctrine, but also an empirical hypothesis of some real explanatory power. Empiricists in the theory of knowledge accordingly adopted similar ideas. Sense-experience was resolved into elementary constituents, called 'ideas' or 'impressions', and mental life likewise into elementary ideas. The fabric of our knowledge was composed by the combination of ideas, which was governed by a small number of laws of association. To elements and compounds in the external world there corresponded simple and complex ideas in the inner world; as the external world was described in terms of particles and laws of motion, so the inner world of the mind was described in terms of ideas and laws of their association. 'Mental philosophy' was dominated by this 'associationist psychology' from the late seventeenth century until well into the nineteenth.

The associationist psychology had many faults. It did not clearly distinguish logic from psychology. Descriptive talk about how the mind actually *does* work was blended with normative talk about the principles by which the mind *ought* to work, if it is to reason validly. This confusion was compounded by the implicit determinism of the whole theory, which made it difficult to give an adequate account of error. The formalism and daylight clarity of the theory made it unable to recognize how much consciousness is a matter of degree, how much in the life of the mind is obscure, fragmentary and unfocused. It could give no satisfactory account of the creative imagination, or of aesthetic and religious experience. And in particular, it was too static; the idea of a balance of forces suggested a self in equilibrium, and failed to emphasize the striving, forward-moving, seeking drives in personal life. Various words have been used for this aspect of the self: the Buddhists call it 'craving'; Spinoza called it 'conation'; biologists have used words like 'appetition'; and Freud said 'libido'. At any rate, a word is needed for the biological, sub-rational drive which maintains our life, and the nineteenth century recognized the fact. For one of the key ideas of the nineteenth century is that of progress through conflict—development, not just by 'clarification', but through a vast, surging, and only obscurely conscious historic struggle, a kind of tidal wave.

Darwin picked up that idea. He read Malthus, but Malthus

was still dominated by the eighteenth-century idea of a balance of forces. The popular memory of Malthus is a Victorian misconception. People fancy that Malthus said the human race will breed itself up to catastrophe. He said nothing of the kind. He said that in an old country with a stable population the size of the population is the resultant of two forces, the 'power of multiplication' (people's reproductive desires and powers) being precisely balanced by the various 'positive' and 'preventive' checks on the growth of population. In a young, underpopulated country the checks have not yet come fully into operation, but in time they must. Given that there is an absolute limit to the world's agricultural production, there must be an absolute limit to the population which the world can support; and, given that men's desire to reproduce so fast as to increase the total population is an unalterable fact of human nature, then, in the long run, that desire must be frustrated. Complete satisfaction of all our desires on this earth is (if Malthus' assumptions are correct) therefore unattainable, and Utopian doctrines are proved to be untrue.

Malthus' doctrines may be wrong, but that is what he said,[12] and it falls a good way short of what Darwin requires. Malthus denies that version of eighteenth-century optimism which says that the world-order is *already* a perfect harmony, and he also denies the version that says that in the remote future it will *become* one. The world is not perfect now, and can never become so; but nor will history end in an apocalyptic catastrophe. On the contrary, in man's relation to nature there is always a movement towards a stable and more or less painful and imperfect equilibrium. We can accept a measure of frustration in life voluntarily, or we can have it forced upon us, but frustration there will be. Malthus still sees man-in-nature in terms of a balance of forces.

What Darwin adds is twofold. From Lyell's *Principles of Geology* he gets the idea of gradual development over a very long period of time, and the presence in the rock strata of the fossil remains of vast numbers of extinct organisms suggests the

[12] T. R. Malthus, *An Essay on the Principle of Population*, first edition of 1798, together with an introduction, notes, and a reprinting of the *Summary View* of 1730, edited by Anthony Flew. Penguin Books 1970. The second edition of 1803 (revised by Malthus in 1806, 1807, 1817, and 1826) is reprinted in the Everyman's Library edition.

extension of the idea of development from the mineral to the plant and animal kingdoms. And, secondly, he has his country-man's knowledge of variation, and the possibility of selective breeding. Add these ideas to Malthus, and it is possible that Malthus' reproductive urge, beating vainly against immovable limits, may be transmuted into a creative force which can originate new species, and indeed bind together all the phenomena of biology into one vast interpretative scheme. All that is needed is to collect enough information to lay out a cumulative argument.

But still more important to us is the intellectual confidence and assurance that Darwin shows when extending his new methods of explanation to man. He builds up from below, along evolutionary lines; and compared with a modern biologist the range of this reclusive Victorian country gentleman is prodigious. Thus, an account of Darwin's ideas about psychology must begin with his book on *The Power of Movement in Plants* (1881) in which all plant movements are exhibited as evolutionary trans-formations of simple tropisms, responses to stimuli, and the spiral described by the growth-point's circumnutation.[13] The principle of a truly biological psychology is, 'build up from below, by a series of steps each of which is functionally explic-able'. And Darwin moves easily from animals to men not only in such areas as the expression of the emotions, sexual dim-orphism[14] and sexual behaviour, but also in his transition from reproductive behaviour, the care of the young, and social be-haviour, to the territory of ethics proper.[15]

And it is here that we are brought up sharply, as we suddenly enter an area of bitter controversy. Surely at this point Darwin is violating one of the most jealously-guarded of all intellectual frontiers, the line between descriptive studies (which say what *is* the case), and normative studies, such as logic and ethics (which lay down what *ought* to be the case)? What is worse, 'Social Darwinism', applying to society the ideas of the struggle for

[13] Time-lapse photography shows that the growth-point circles as it moves up.

[14] The surprisingly different forms of the two sexes in many species.

[15] Charles Darwin, *The Descent of Man and Selection in Relation to Sex*, 2nd edn (London, John Murray 1888), Volume II, esp. pp. 426-30.

existence and the survival of the fittest, sought to justify militarism: 'By means of the struggle the élites are continually renewed. The law of selection justifies this incessant struggle by allowing the survival of the fittest.' Any kind of compassion for the weak has deleterious effects on the health of society: 'Taken to its logical extreme Christianity would mean the systematic cult of human failure.'[16]

We can, however, defend Darwin himself from the imputation of guilt by association with Hitler's Social Darwinism. All he is saying is that human conduct has grown out of animal behaviour, and that some or many human moral institutions are biologically advantageous and so biologically explicable. There are resemblances, and indeed historical affinities, between pair-bonding to provide for the care of the young in animals and the human institutions of marriage and the family, and between social organization in gregarious animals and human co-operation. A religious moralist need not dispute this. It is true that in religion institutions such as marriage, the family and social co-operation are commonly regarded as divinely ordained, but the divine ordinance of cultural institutions is not incompatible with their gradual development from biological forerunners, if the creator of man is also the creator of nature. In traditional religious thought, Christian and other, the natural moral law which leads men to strive to maintain their lives, to seek to reproduce themselves, and to co-operate with their fellows, has commonly been regarded as a divine blessing and ratification of fundamental biological needs. Other moral claims may on occasion override them, so that an individual may be obliged to become an ascetic, a celibate, or a solitary, but the basic drives to self-preservation, sex and social co-operation have commonly been regarded (at least in religions which have a doctrine of creation) as both biologically advantageous and (other things being equal) morally good and right. So Darwin's procedure in moving from evolution to ethics is not *necessarily* either bad logic or bad religion. Even in a *strictly* ethical justification of marriage it would not be either irrelevant or irreligious to mention the biological advantages of monogamy—especially in

[16] Adolf Hitler, cited in A. G. N. Flew, *Evolutionary Ethics* (London, Macmillan 1967), p. 36.

53

societies where life is harsh and medicine poorly-developed—in providing as secure an environment as possible for the raising of the young. The most formal, rigorous and traditional book on marriage in the English language makes precisely these points.[17] 'Evolutionary ethics' becomes logically and religiously objectionable only when it crudely *identifies* biological explanation with properly ethical justification.

In this chapter we have pointed to three strands in the development of the sciences of man: the development of modern medicine, the gradual application of statistics to human affairs, and the displacement of mechanical by Darwinian forms of explanation. These three themes by no means exhaust the subject, but they are all important, and they all have still a good deal of life in them.

What of the fears which surround the application of the scientific method to man? The issue of freedom must be deferred to the next chapter, but some of the others can be summarily disposed of now, for they are plainly unjustified. The fear of medical omnipotence and arrogance is largely irrational, and can be dismissed so long as our legislators and we ourselves do not allow the medical men to become isolated, but keep an intelligent eye on what they are doing. The fear of manipulation is little more than a reluctance to accept our own bodiliness. Insofar as we are physical objects which behave in predictable ways, to know as much is a gain, and a defence against manipulation. Every great religion says, 'Know thyself', and it is unfortunate that religious techniques of self-examination have not kept pace with our growing knowledge. Too often religious people appear to lack self-awareness, rather than, as they should, have it in the highest degree. Again, that God builds up the world from below, out of humble materials, is common religious doctrine, so there is no good reason why people should be alarmed or surprised to learn that their attitude to God historically grows out of their early feelings about their parents, or that much of the psychic energy that is put into religion is erotic in source. Nor is there any reason to be surprised that many people acquire their beliefs, and not least their religious

[17] T. A. Lacey, *Marriage in Church and State*, revised and supplemented by R. C. Mortimer (London, S.P.C.K. 1947), e.g., p. 2f.

beliefs, in non-rational ways. There are few difficulties here that cannot be overcome by a greater love for the physical world, a deeper respect for biological reality, and a love of truth.

But the questions about the nature of freedom, and consciousness, are more profound and important.

DISCUSSION QUESTIONS

Insofar as the scientific method is successfully applied to the study of man, must it tend to weaken our confidence in human freedom and rationality? For example, is our confidence in the democratic process in any way affected by the success of predictions of voting behaviour?

Are there or should there be religious or ethical limits to the scientific study of man by man?

5

BUS OR TRAM?

There was a young man who said, 'Damn!
At last I've found out that I am
A creature that moves
In determinate grooves—
In fact not a bus, but a tram'.

As we look about us we seem to see a world which is in every respect perfectly determinate. The tree outside the window has a certain definite number of leaves on it, no more, no less. The book beside me on the desk has a certain number of black marks impressed upon its pages, is of certain dimensions, of a certain chemical composition, and so on. It is true that there is a risk of error, or an inevitable imprecision, in all human acts of measurement. If a dozen of us sat down, each to count the number of characters printed on the pages of the book, we should doubtless come up with slightly differing totals. But this admitted fact of human error does not affect our conviction that there is a definite total. From time to time there is a fresh attempt to determine the velocity of light more accurately than it has been determined hitherto. The units in which that velocity is defined (centimetres and seconds), and the velocity itself, are capable of ever more exact definition. The value for the velocity of light with which physicists operate is an approximation, and we can continue to make the approximation closer and closer; but though it is, inescapably, only an approximation, nevertheless the velocity of light does have (physicists suppose) a precise and determinate value, just as π has a determinate value, even though we cannot completely determine it. There is, then, for various reasons, always a small margin of error in our map of the world, but the world itself seems fully determinate.

And all physical changes in the world seem to take place in determinate ways, according to universal rules which are, to some extent at least, discoverable by us. In prescientific cultures untoward events were often ascribed to the agency of spirits, which might act more or less capriciously and inexplicably. But in our own culture it has long been an established maxim, followed with striking success, that when an untoward event occurs it can very often be reproduced experimentally, investigated, and shown to be rule-governed. So events such as the appearance of a comet, the occurrence of a thunderstorm, the apparent bending of an oar dipped in water, and so on have proved capable of explanation as occurring in accordance with rules. Admittedly our knowledge of the rules is more exact in some cases than in others. I have just been reading the morning paper, and have found in it predictions about the time of sunset, the day's weather, the likely extinction of a certain species of bird, and the future course of the British economy. We are all agreed that these four types of prediction are listed in descending order of reliability, astronomical prediction being highly reliable, and economic prediction very uncertain. In the case of the prediction of the hour of sunset, the factors determining when the sun will set are simple and easy to analyse, whereas in the case of economics the data are complex and difficult to analyse. But we can surely say that economic events are in themselves perfectly determinate, and can, in principle at least, be explained as the outcome of previous events. Insofar as economics is, or can hope to become, a science, it must suppose that economic events are intelligible, and intelligibility just means capability of causal explanation.

Determinism, then, is the view that all events are caused. For every event or state of affairs in the universe there is some preceding event or state of affairs connected with it in such a way that when this latter occurs, then the former must occur, the connection being always in accordance with a rule which states that events of type A are always followed by events of type B.

What we have said so far already suggests, however, various slightly different interpretations of determinism. Thus determinism might be regarded as true *a priori*, as a necessity of reason. The philosopher Kant considered that to know the world at all we *must* understand it as a system of bodies moving about in Euclidean space in accordance with universal laws of nature. More cautiously, we might say that determinism is a presumption and an ideal of scientific method. It would be objectively validated only if the scientific map of the world were known to be complete and not further corrigible, but such a state is an ideal limit, never in practice reached, and perhaps unattainable. In some areas greater precision is possible than in others, but it would be going beyond the evidence to claim that the movements of a stray dog about the town will one day be as predictable as the movement of Mars about the Sun. All we can do is press the scientific method as far as we can; and at the point where it is plainly yielding diminishing returns we may conclude that we are reaching the limits of the usefulness of a deterministic model of nature. The third possible interpretation of determinism is that it is not a philosophical doctrine but a scientific hypothesis, largely vindicated in physics and the sciences closest to it, and, insofar as the other sciences are reducible to physics, thereby shown actually to be true of the world itself.

Is determinism, then, a scientific hypothesis? Classical mechanics *was* deterministic, and (in alliance with John Locke's philosophy) held that the world-process was completely deterministic.[1] Newton's mechanics operated with a limited number of basic concepts: space, time, particle, velocity, gravitational attraction, momentum, elasticity and so on. It could pretend to give a *complete* account of the world only if all our other basic empirical concepts are reducible to those of Newtonian mechanics. Locke's philosophy suggested that this was so; substances could be treated as aggregations of particles, colours and sounds as subjective effects of the impact of particles on the retina and eardrum, and so on. It seemed then that Newtonian mechanics could give a deterministic account, not merely of some aspects of the physical world, but of that world as a whole.

But is modern physics deterministic? Controversy on this point is intense, and highly technical. In classical (i.e., Newtonian) mechanics it was held that a precise state-description of a physical system and a precise knowledge of the laws of motion were possible, so that predictions of future states of the system could be rigorously exact. But in quantum mechanics

[1] See J. R. Lucas, *The Freedom of the Will* (O.U.P. 1970), § 16.

it is acknowledged that our statements about the behaviour of bodies (most notably where very small-scale events are concerned) have to be statistical, that is, expressed in terms of probabilities. Given a lump of radioactive material, we can say with some accuracy at what rate it will decay, but we cannot predict just when a particular atom will decay. We can only describe a probability. The controversy revolves mainly round the question whether the probabilistic character of modern physics is subjective (i.e., based on inescapable limitations in ourselves as observers), or an objective feature of the world.

Here are two examples of arguments on each side.[2] First, imagine an open-topped box partitioned across the middle by a very fine knife-edge which divides it into left and right compartments. Above it there is a chute down which balls roll to fall into the box. This chute can traverse so as to aim the balls, first into the right-hand compartment, then directly on to the knife-edge, and then into the left-hand compartment. As the chute is moved across the box we find that at first all the balls fall into the right-hand compartment. There follows a phase when the balls strike the knife-edge, some falling to the right and some to the left, and finally all the balls fall to the left.

The intermediate phase, when some balls fall to the right and some to the left, has a very small but finite angular width: let us call it $\Delta\alpha$. At the moment when the chute *enters* this region the proportion of left-falling to right-falling balls is $0:100$. At the moment when the chute *leaves* this region, it is $100:0$.

If determinism were true, and the world quite cut-and-dried, we might expect to pass direct from $0:100$ to $100:0$, with perhaps an instant, $\delta\alpha$ (an infinitesimal angular width), at which the ball remains resting on the knife-edge. But in fact there is a phase of finite width $\Delta\alpha$, and within that phase what occurs conforms to mathematical random theory. If the determinist says, yes, but could we but trace the minutest details of the shape of the balls, the spin they gather, atmospheric perturbation and so on, we would be able to determine precisely which way each ball must fall, then the reply is, no, as we go back in the causal

[2] Taken from the articles by M. K. Munitz and D. W. Sciama in Sidney Hook, ed., *Determinism and Freedom in the Age of Modern Science*. New York, Collier Books 1961.

chains, and get down to minuter events, we do not dispel the element of random—we find more of it. However far we go back, there is a persistent and irreducible element of random in the structure of the world. And that is what quantum physics is saying.

In other sciences we are perfectly used to this state of affairs. A colleague of mine is studying a particular species of Arctic sea-bird mathematically. The whole world-population of this bird uses only a few great nesting-sites, and he can keep records of a largish sample of birds at all of them. He wants to map their genetics and economics in detail, so as to make a mathematical picture of natural selection at work. But of course he deals *entirely* in probabilities, which (because of the finite population size) contains a substantial margin of error. Consider questions like these: Will a particular male find a good nesting-site? Which female will choose him? How many eggs will she lay? How many young will they raise to maturity? How will those young differ from each other? Which of them will survive and which succumb to predators, hunger, disease or accident? His mathematical model of natural selection at work will be constructed entirely in terms of probabilities.

To this biologist determinism is a non-issue. He deals in probabilities, and would go on doing so even if the physicists decided they were after all thoroughgoing determinists. The phenomenon he is studying admits of being studied only in terms of probabilities.

None of all this, however, is of much advantage to the libertarian, whose interest is in human freedom of thought and action. Indeterminable events which, taken in bulk, conform to the mathematical theory of probability, are not at all the same kind of thing as free and rational human judgements, and actions. All that the indeterminist has shown is that the structure of the world is not rigid and clear-cut like a formal system, but contains an element of sheer contingency. And in any case, randomness at the sub-microscopic level might (and in physics usually does) coexist with a high degree of predictability at the macroscopic level.

Our second example points the other way. It is an attempt to reconcile quantum physics with determinism. In classical mechanics it was held that, given a complete description of a closed physical system at time t, and enough boundary conditions (conditions limiting and determing the behaviour of the system) then all future states of the system at t_1, t_2, etc., could be computed. But let us suppose that in quantum mechanics the world is still deterministic, but we need to know some *future* boundary conditions as well as some past ones in order to determine it at a given moment. However, the observer, within the system, knows only the past. So when he tries to make a prediction about the future he does not have all the requisite data. They are hidden from him, and the system appears to be partly indeterminate. So he averages over the boundary conditions that are known to him, and makes a forward projection; that is, he introduces a probability calculus. And this probability-calculus is quantum mechanics.

This suggestion has some resemblance to older philosophical doctrines, for example in Leibniz.[3] To God, an eternal and infinite mind outside the temporal process to whom it is all timelessly present, the whole world-process appears deterministic, and indeed he has himself determined it in every detail. But to us, within the process, with finite intellects and ignorant of the future, the world-process does not appear fully deterministic, and the future course of our own lives is hidden from us. We can act as being, or as if we were, free agents.

We will discuss the question of God and predestination in a moment, but in the meanwhile we have to form some opinions about determinism in science.

Is the universe, then, deterministic in a strong sense? In the case of classical mechanics we noted that it had to be conjoined with Locke's philosophy to generate thoroughgoing physical determinism. For Locke argued that the secondary qualities of bodies, such as colour and noisiness, though not as such represented in Newton's mechanics, could be 'resolved' into concepts which *are* represented in Newton's mechanics. The bold, highly metaphysical dream was that all life—not just natural science, but ethics, politics and human thought and feeling—could all be boiled down to classical mechanics. Thomas Hobbes and Jeremy Bentham were English philosophers who

[3] G. W. Leibniz (1646–1716), philosopher and mathematician.

61

gave a rough intimation of what the result might be, and Émile Zola was a late example of a novelist influenced by deterministic ideas.

The analogous claim today would run something like this: libertarians say that physical determinism can never undermine our belief in our own freedom of thought and action, because a purely physical description of physical events can never be a complete description of someone thinking, deciding and acting, for the same physical motions may be constituents of very different actions. But the determinist may reply that you cannot *wholly* disjoin physical behaviour from moral action, as Kant came near to doing. Some descriptions of bits of physical behaviour are at least incompatible with a description of a piece of conduct as a moral action. And besides, the determinist will want to extend his description into the nervous system and brain processes, giving in the end a very elaborate physical description of a piece of human behaviour in terms of initial conditions, stimuli and responses.[4] He says that the scientific method must in the end eliminate 'final causes', not merely from nature, but also from man. Loose talk about birds picking up twigs 'in order to' build nests has to be replaced by more exact talk about certain behaviour-patterns being triggered by hormones, which in turn are stimulated by courtship behaviour and the lengthening hours of daylight. Similarly, loose talk about human behaviour in terms of goals and intentions will be translated into a more exact language of stimulus and response.

There are differing views as to how far such a programme can really be carried out without absurdity. My own belief is that the programme *is* absurd, because the more seriously it is taken, the more alienated the psychologist himself becomes from the humanity which he studies. Of course there are large elements of the caused and the impersonal in human life. Of all the fabulously complex events which daily take place in my body, only a very few may be counted as rational thought and moral decision, but those few are of great metaphysical importance, and it is ludicrous to try to eliminate them, when we must

[4] See B. A. O. Williams in D. F. Pears, ed., *The Freedom of the Will* (London, Macmillan 1963), esp. pp. 110f.

presuppose them in order to make the attempt. In order to construct hypotheses and test them, to design and conduct experiments and evaluate their results, the psychologist must presuppose his own rationality and freedom of action. He cannot suppose that the logical distinctions between valid and invalid reasoning, true and false propositions, are *identical* with the occurrence of this or that chemical event, if indeed such a supposition is even intelligible.[5] He could not seriously conduct a dispute with a colleague if he thought that his opinion was a chemical process in his brain, and his colleague's opinion was a chemical process in *his* brain. How can one chemical process contradict another?

Many other points are made by commentators on physical determinism. It cannot be a *complete* explanation of the world, for it cannot explain the initial conditions and the physical laws at the beginning of the world-process, but must take them for granted. We can always ask, why *this* initial configuration, and not some other? Not all possibilities are realized; the genetic complexity of human beings is such that only a fraction of all the possible genetically-different human beings can ever be born. So why some, and not the others? Many have pointed out the paradoxes of prediction, on which physical determinism lays such stress. How, for example, can I predict a *discovery*? To *predict* a discovery would be to *make* it. A physical determinist must find it hard to cope with real novelty in the world-process. Again, as every politician knows, to make a prediction about the future is to introduce a new causal factor into the present situation. So it is necessary to recalculate to take account of the difference made by the publication of the prediction. But when the recalculation is published, it too will make a difference, so recalculation will have to go on until the future moment envisaged has arrived, by which time it is no longer a *prediction*!

These reasons may well lead us to prefer the *second* view about determinism mentioned on page 58 above, and say, (a) that determinism is a methodological postulate of the sciences; (b) that the physical determinism which proposes to reduce *all* the sciences to (a deterministically-understood) physics is impossibly

[5] See Norman Malcolm in C. V. Borst, ed., *The Mind-Brain Identity Theory* (London, Macmillan 1970), pp. 171ff.

63

paradoxical; (c) that our picture of the world must take account of human freedom and rationality, which indeed are presupposed by the scientific method itself; and (d), that physical cosmology cannot give a *complete* account of why we have the world we have, rather than some other world, or no world at all, for it must always stop at some initial configuration of things which it cannot further explain.

But if we reject a rigorously mechanistic physical determinism, which speaks solely of antecedent efficient causes, and embrace instead a wider notion of 'cause', then the sting of determinism is drawn. One sometimes hears biologists airing a sort of 'genetic determinism', but this is very loose, for no one can claim that the lives of identical twins are identical in every detail. Freud and other psychologists have espoused a kind of psychological determinism, but Freud's language is metaphorical (he does not seem to have been a strict materialist, and indeed it would be difficult to give a materialist interpretation to his system), and he can scarcely claim to be able to predict *in detail* the future course of his patients' lives. Marxists and sociologists use the language of determinism, but they have become wary of specific predictions. Non-physical, non-reductive determinism is doing little more than emphasize how much of our behaviour is moulded by heredity, by our emotional make-up, by group-pressures, and so on. These things are worth saying, and worth taking to heart, but that the world, and the chains of habit, can *diminish* our freedom is scarcely a novel idea; the issue is whether they preclude it absolutely.

If our notion of explanation, and of cause, widens to allow the reasonableness of citing the agent's *intentions* in explaining his behaviour, the way may be reopened to explaining the world in terms, not just of efficient causes, but of final causes, or purposes. They figure, after all, in historical explanation, and our picture of the cosmic process is in a sense 'historical' nowadays; so they cannot be ruled out in advance as absurd or superstitious. What clearer kind of explanation of a puzzling piece of behaviour can there be than that the agent rationally chose to do this thing because by doing it he could attain some great good? Along these lines we may be led to consider an old and grand form of determinism, the claim that every detail of the world-process has been determined by an all-powerful, all-wise and all-good Creator. As an example of such a view we may take someone already mentioned, G. W. Leibniz, who, although very much a product of the scientific revolution, firmly believed in final causes, thinking that an explanation of the universe wholly satisfying to the intellect must be theological.

According to Leibniz, all 'our reasonings are founded upon two great principles, that of contradiction ... and that of sufficient reason, in virtue of which we hold that there can be no fact real or existing, no statement true, unless there be a sufficient reason why it should be so and not otherwise' (*Monadology*, § 31, 32[6]). The complexity of the world is such that only an infinite intellect can know the sufficient reason of all things, but that there must *be* one is a requirement of reason.

To the principle of contradiction correspond the truths of reasoning, that is, the *a priori* truths of logic and mathematics, whose opposites are impossible. Leibniz sees these eternal truths as subsisting eternally in the divine understanding. Truths of fact, on the other hand, are contingent; it is conceivable that they might have been other than they are. They depend upon the divine will, and the principle of sufficient reason which governs God's choice of them.

We can now briefly set out Leibniz' proof of God. It is this: If the world is intelligible, God exists. But the world is intelligible; therefore God exists. In a fuller form, it can be expressed thus:

1. There is a sufficient reason why everything that is, is so and not otherwise. That is, whenever there are several logically possible alternatives, there is a sufficient reason why the alternative realized is the one realized.

2. Sufficient reasons are either causes or choices or both.

3. Of any cause, as distinct from choice, one can always ask what its cause is.

4. Hence causes cannot be ultimately sufficient reasons.

5. Now the actual universe is not the only possible universe.

6. Hence (by 1, 2, 4) its sufficient reason must be a choice.

[6] R. Latta, ed., *Leibniz: The Monadology and other Philosophical Writings* (O.U.P. 1898), pp. 235ff.

7. But choices are sufficient reasons only insofar as they are rational choices.

8. A choice is rational insofar as it is a choice of the best; and if the chooser is limited in power or knowledge his choice is rational only relative to those limits, and requires further explanation.

9. Therefore an absolutely rational choice, requiring no further explanation, is a choice of the best, made by a being subject to no limitations.

10. Therefore (by 5, 6, 9 and the definition of God) God exists.[7]

Now let us see how Leibniz treats the freedom of God the creator, and of man as creature. For the first, Leibniz intended to correct his great predecessor, Spinoza, who had denied divine freedom outright. Though also a rationalist, Leibniz wants to retain the freedom of God. So he says, in the orthodox manner, that God is indeed not free to change the eternal truths (this is no limitation, for they are the very forms of his own understanding), but his decision to create the world is free, and not logically necessitated. He creates by the generous overflow of his own goodness. But, given that he will create, and his intellect and power of choice are unlimited, he is presented with an infinite number of possible worlds to create. He riffles through them all, his wisdom shows him which is best, and his goodness leads him to actualize it. The one he chooses must be that which contains the greatest amount of moral and metaphysical perfection.

There is of course no arbitrariness in God's freedom; the highest liberty is to act perfectly, according to sovereign reason.[8] God's goodness and perfection 'oblige' him to choose the best world, but he is not logically necessitated, nor obliged by anything other than himself, so his choice of the best world is a free and praiseworthy expression of his own goodness.

If we say to Leibniz, 'Would it not have been better for God to have created a world in every respect identical with this one, but without just one evil action A?', then Leibniz replies that if A were different, everything else in the universe would be different too, because everything is interlocked with everything

[7] Slightly modified from Wallace I. Matson, *The Existence of God* (Ithaca, N.Y., Cornell U.P. 1967), p. 74.

[8] *Discourse on Metaphysics* (1686), § III.

66

else. And God decided that the world-with-A was on the whole better than the different world-without-A.

For Leibniz the world is composed of an immeasurable number of distinct simple substances, each of which has its entire life-history folded up in itself, and each of which mirrors the entire universe from its own point of view. To give a complete account of anything is, by implication, to give a complete account of everything. To change one thing, you must change everything. God chose the best possible set of jointly-possible things. And of course his infinite intellect knows and foreordains the minutest details of the universe.

What then of human freedom? Many libertarians say that a man is not free unless, all other things being equal, he could have acted otherwise. Leibniz denies this. If Judas had acted otherwise, the whole world would have been different, and Judas would have been different. In eternity God pre-envisaged the whole course of Judas' life in this world, seeing every bit of it continuously connected with every other bit and harmonized with the life histories of all other creatures. And he chose to bring sinning Judas into being. Judas' sin, thereafter, proceeds from the unfolding of Judas' own nature. It is *his*, analytically; he commits it freely, of himself, and, given *this* world, there is no sense in saying that he could have done otherwise. A non-sinning Judas would be someone else, in another world. In this world Judas is what he is, having the place he has in the whole scheme of things.

And that is Leibniz' account of that fearful saying in the Gospel, 'The Son of Man goes as it is written of him, but woe to that man by whom the Son of Man is betrayed! It would have been better for that man if he had not been born' (Matt. 26.24).[9]

Leibniz' account of God's foreordination and man's freedom differs in flavour from that of the great biblical and ecclesiastical writers, such as Paul, Augustine and Calvin. But it has for our purposes the advantage of being a mathematician's account. The

[9] For Leibniz, see P. G. Lucas and L. Grint, eds., *Discourse on Metaphysics*. Manchester U.P. 1968; H. T. Mason, ed., The Leibniz-Arnauld Correspondence. Manchester U.P. 1967; and Austin Farrer, ed., *Theodicy*. London, Routledge 1951. See also Godfrey Vesey, ed., *Philosophy in the Open University* (Open University Press 1974), Chapter 2.

way he speaks is more intelligible to someone trained in the natural sciences and mathematics than is the way Calvin speaks. And what Leibniz says, creates, I believe, a dilemma, forcing a choice between two different ways of conceiving God's relation to the world. We can illustrate them with two parables.

In the first, a film director has been shooting a film. During shooting a good deal of rewriting and even recasting went on, and the director found himself with a large stock of 'rushes', not all compatible with each other. In the end he has assembled, out of them, several different versions, which are all sitting in their cans. He needs to choose one for release, so he runs them all through, and chooses the best. That one is then released for public exhibition. Some good rushes have had to be discarded, but if they cannot be worked in without spoiling the coherence of the whole, that cannot be helped. Within the chosen version the personae must act plausibly and stay 'in character'. It makes no sense to ask that the heroine at some point behave differently, for that would be to ask for one of the suppressed versions, and the director has already chosen the best. The artistic coherence and unity of the whole is the primary thing to be borne in mind, and it is as a *whole* that the director has compiled and chosen the film.

That parable represents Leibniz' account, first given, by the way, at least as early as Origen.[10] The other parable describes a novelist, the sort of novelist who does not preplan his novel in great detail in advance, but begins with a setting, a range of characters, and a theme, and lets the plot work itself out in the writing, as he goes along. He sets the scene and introduces the characters, and as he lives with them in imagination day by day they take on more definite shape in his mind. He is able to let them loose on the page, to let *them* determine the details of the plot as he writes. The theme of the novel is his, everything remains under his control, and he is going to ensure that it is properly rounded off, but within that overall framework

[10] E. G. Jay, ed., *Treatise on Prayer* (c. A.D. 236) (London, S.P.C.K. 1954), pp. 92-104. Origen reconciles intercessory prayer with divine foreknowledge by saying that both the prayer and its answer are included in God's eternal plan, so that the prayer does not change God's plan, but implements it.

he is content to let the characters work out their own destinies.

In the first parable there is a clear distinction between the planning of the world, and the effecting of the plan. In the second parable the planning and the creating are simultaneous; there is no clear distinction between God's knowledge, and his action. His thinking of the world is his making of it.[11] In the first parable God's omnipotence and omniscience are shown in his prior determination and election of every detail of the world-process. In the second they are shown in the very self-restraint by which he is able to allow the world-process to unfold itself, while yet being certain of being able to guide it towards the conclusion he intends.

This second picture is less mathematical, and more anthropomorphic, but, within its limits—and it is only a picture—it gives a better account of freedom, and is perhaps closer to theistic religious tradition and experience. Our scientific picture of nature nowadays emphasizes the flow of time more than in Leibniz' day, so it may be closer to modern science, too.

DISCUSSION QUESTIONS

Why have some Christian believers denied the freedom of the will?

How is such denial, whether by Puritans or Marxists, combined with a very active, this-worldly ethic?

If, for God, the future is as fully determinate as the past, what is the difference between past and future? Is it possible for a believer in God to hold that the future is unknowable even by omniscience?

[11] The two parables each have a long tradition behind them. Ancient Christian and Jewish thought, borrowing from classical philosophy, located the Platonic world of Ideas in the divine mind. These Ideas were 'exemplary causes', blueprints for creatures. This suggests a clear distinction between God's planning of the world and his creating of it. But others, wanting to emphasize the divine unity, felt they must deny the distinction and say that in God knowledge and activity must be identical. For a brief introduction, see A. H. Armstrong and R. A. Markus, *Christian Faith and Greek Philosophy* (London, Darton, Longman & Todd 1960), Chs. 1-4.

6

TECHNICAL AND RITUAL OPERATIONS

Of all culinary operations, making tea might be thought one of the simplest, but in England (as in Japan) it manages to become quite a complex procedure. The water is boiled in one vessel, poured on the leaves in another, and decanted for drinking into a third. People repeat many traditional proverbs governing tea-making, which lay down that you must begin with cold water, not watch the kettle, warm the teapot, put in a teaspoonful of leaves for each person and one for the pot, leave the tea to brew, mash or stand for five minutes, and so on.

The first inclination of a critical observer is to ask which items in this performance are *necessary* to the making of a good cup of tea, and which are 'mere' ritual elaboration. To ask that question is to betray the influence of the scientific method. It is not always easy to answer. I do not know whether it makes a perceptible difference to the flavour (and so is a functional matter) if the milk goes into the cup first or second, or whether it is 'mere' ritual.

But people certainly make the distinction. The technical operations are rational or functional. They are considered to be causal conditions for attaining the desired end-product. The ritual elements, by contrast, are irrational or non-functional, symbolic ('one for the pot'), prescribed by tradition ('my mother always used to say'), and mnemonic ('you'll get it right if you always remember to do it in this order . . .'). But this distinction is very rough and ready, and any apprentice to a craft soon learns that purely technical operations have to be performed in a traditionally-prescribed order.

And why do we drink tea at all? It has, by itself, no nutritive value. Still more curious is the connection between tea and social class. Like so many other goods, tea carries class overtones. Twining's or Typhoo; China or Indian; weak or strong; plain, with lemon or with milk; milk in first, or tea in first—the whole bizarre British class-system is expressed in miniature in tea-rituals, thus bearing out the anthropologists' observation that ritual actions are symbolic statements about the social order.

Let us now consider a slightly more elevated example, the procedure in a court of law. Here the 'rational' element is the systematic presentation of evidence and arguments by the prosecution and the defence, while the judge superintends the proceedings and, with the jury, evaluates the case. The 'ritual' element is very marked indeed, in the layout of the courtroom, the precise ordering of the stages, the verbal formulae that mark transitions, the curious dress of the key officials, and so on. Some people express impatience with all this ritual, and regard it as flummery, but in fact it is of great importance, for it defines symbolically the context within which the legal proceedings are carried on. The man on the bench is no longer John Smith, a bare forked animal, but the judge, an embodiment of reason, the majestic impartiality of the law. The ritual makes general statements about the nature of the law, about the rule of law, about the impartial administration of justice, about the need to bear true witness, and about moral responsibility, and it assigns his place in the drama to each person present. The ritual is not exempt from criticism; it can be changed, and is admittedly different in different countries. But it does not follow (as some sceptics who point to the diversity of religious symbolism and ritual seem to think) that it is unimportant or empty. On the contrary, it defines the entire framework within which the law is administered.

In these two examples, of tea-making and the law court, the technical (functional or rational) and the ritual (symbolic or supposedly 'irrational') elements in the whole performance seem very closely interwoven. But in our culture people do distinguish them, and very often in such a way as to put ritual on the defensive. It is assumed that a technical operation is the paradigm of a rational action, and then asked, how can ritual acts be justified? What kind of efficacy, if any, can be attributed to prayers and sacrifices? The distinctive achievement of

71

Western culture, which makes us call it *scientific*, surely depends upon the progressive replacement of ritual performances based on religious belief by technical operations based on scientific knowledge, in one sphere of life after another. So what is the *use* of ritual? Once, men reckoned that the growth of their crops depended upon the gods, and sought the blessing of fertility by ritual performances. But with the growth of scientific agriculture, prayers for rain and a good harvest have been replaced by technical operations. So why continue to perform any rituals at all? To analyse this issue is to gain a clearer insight into what the science-and-religion issue means in practical terms.

Ritual is defined as 'any form of behaviour the characteristics of which are fixed by tradition. In the study of religion it means "traditional religious behaviour or actions", in which sense it is close in meaning to "cult" '.[1] In the wider meaning the term ritual embraces almost the whole subject-matter of social anthropology, anything that is, in Durkheim's phrase, 'a social fact', something true of a whole society rather than just an individual member of it. Thus, my wearing trousers is a social fact; they are the prescribed dress for men in my society. If you want an explanation of why I wear trousers, it has to be sociological, rather than in terms of my personal preference.

In the narrower meaning of ritual, the sense in which it is close to 'cult', it may include magic, witchcraft, religious customs, sacrifice, sacraments and prayers. In Western Europe ritual has a narrower meaning still, for it denotes the prescribed form of *words* to be used in some liturgical function, as distinct from *ceremonial*, the prescribed dress, actions and so on.

Debate about ritual action, why it must be done duly or correctly, and what the use of it is, has a very long history, and there are many different traditions of discussion. Since religious rituals are the visible expressions of religious beliefs, when a change in religious belief occurs it is always accompanied by ritual change. Religious reformers criticize the old rituals. The most famous examples are the classical Israelite prophets,[2] but

[1] E. J. Sharpe, *Fifty Key Words: Comparative Religion* (London, Lutterworth Press 1971), *s.v.*

[2] E.g., Amos 4.4,5; 5.21-4; Hos. 6.6; 8.11-13; Isa. 1.10-17; Mic. 6.6-8; Jer. 6.20; 7.21-8, etc.

similar criticism of religious rituals can be found in quite different traditions such as that of Confucius and his followers in China. Hsun Tzü is the most notable.[3]

Somewhat different is the philosophical criticism of ritual which began in ancient Greece, and has continued sporadically in the West ever since. Heraclitus of Ephesus (c. 540–480 B.C.) is the earliest philosophical critic of ritual we know of. He is reported to have attacked those who 'vainly try to purify themselves of blood-guilt by defiling themselves with blood, as though one who had stepped into mud were to wash with mud'. In his surviving sayings about popular religion he suggests that its rites are irrational and unedifying; the most he will allow is that they may almost by accident convey an inkling of the truth.[4]

Heraclitus here sets the tone for much of ancient philosophy. Common men vainly suppose that their rituals and prayers will change the dispositions of the gods towards men, and alter what would otherwise have been the course of events. But it is superstition to imagine that the gods can be influenced in this way. Nothing can please the gods but a good life. If we say prayers and perform rituals we can only think of them as changing *us*, bringing us to accept the unchanging divine order of things, and strengthening our resolve to live the good life. Such, by and large, has been the philosophical attitude to prayer.

The narrowest meaning of ritual, which distinguishes rites from ceremonies, helps us make a point here. In ancient religious texts, such as the Jewish Torah, a great many ceremonies are prescribed, but rather few ritual forms of words. Later, however, there is a perceptible shift from ceremonies to rites, from ceremonial action to linguistic action. Early Christian sacramentaries and manuals contain detailed verbal formulae, but few rubrics (rubrics are ceremonial directions, traditionally written in red in Christian service books). This is in line with the philosophers, who are more friendly to prayers than to ceremonial actions. The early Christian philosopher Origen, in the book we have already mentioned, stresses the way

[3] Ninian Smart, *The Religious Experience of Mankind* (London, Collins 1971), p. 210; see also p. 206, on Mo Tzü.
[4] See Kirk and Raven, *The PreSocratic Philosophers* (cited above), pp. 211f.

73

the words for prayer also mean *vow*, thus assimilating prayers to moral resolutions, and emphasizing that prayer is not like a magical or quasi-technical operation. But this shift, from ceremonies to words—a process of internalization—is not consistent. Ceremony returns in medieval Christianity and in Talmudic Judaism, and in due course again excites the scorn of the philosophers. Thus Edward Gibbon, Immanuel Kant and the young Hegel are examples of Enlightenment thinkers who are highly critical of religious ceremonial.[5]

The philosophers have always imputed to the masses the erroneous causal belief that ritual makes the sun rise, the soil fertile, and the soul pure in a rather mechanical way. But modern anthropologists protest against this. Not only is ritual a much more pervasive feature of social life than the philosophers have realized, but also, what prescientific man was trying to do was not to manipulate the gods, or the sun, or the rain, but rather to establish and to enact a proper harmony between earth and heaven, between social life here below and the perceived cosmic order.

So we turn to what the anthropologists make of ritual. Modern anthropology begins with E. B. Tylor's *Primitive Culture* (1871), and the story of the anthropologists' attitudes to ritual since then is an intriguing sidelight on the issue of science and religion.

Tylor himself regarded religion as bad science, and rituals as expressing the erroneous magical or animistic beliefs in which early men were trapped. People's understanding of causal relations was inchoate and confused, and very often likenesses and analogies were mistaken for real causal connections. Why then, we must ask Tylor, do rituals survive so long, if they are ineffectual and based on untrue beliefs? He replies[6] that the ritual may appear to 'work', perhaps because of some real virtue in the performance, or by coincidence, or by trickery, and if the ritual fails it may be said that it was not performed correctly, or the god was displeased, or that someone was practising counter-magic. In any case, before the scientific

[5] Kant is especially vituperative, in *Religion within the Limits of Reason Alone* (1793), Book Four.
[6] E. B. Tylor, *Primitive Culture*, (London, John Murray, 2nd edn 1873), Vol. I, pp. 133ff.

method was developed, people had a more vivid memory of the few occasions when the ritual seemed to work than of the many times when it failed.

In short, Tylor sees religious rituals rather as most of us now would see the wearing of a copper bracelet to alleviate rheumatic pains, or some other unjustifiable and superstitious practice. Religion and magic are bad science, and religious operations are pseudo-technical operations performed under the influence of mistaken beliefs about the course of nature.

A generation later, people were taking a quite different view. Instead of saying that religion was bad, primitive or mistaken science, they began to say that it was not trying to be science at all. Philosophers took up emotive theories of religion, such as appear in the young Bertrand Russell's contrast between science and mysticism[7], and anthropologists began to put forward emotive theories of ritual. 'Savage religion is something not so much thought out as danced out', in Marrett's well-known words;[8] and rituals enact not ideas, but feelings. Freud is the most extreme emotivist, but Bronislaw Malinowski and many others say very similar things. The function of ritual is cathartic. It may be compared with the 'English' which the bowls-player puts on as his wood nears the jack. He gestures strenuously, and speaks to his wood, urging it on. He doesn't seriously attribute causal efficacy to this performance, but it relieves his feelings.[9] So the ritual washing-away of defilement and sin may be compared (as it was by Freud) with Lady Macbeth's compulsive gestures of handwashing.

The obvious difficulty with this theory is that although there are doubtless some cases of ritual behaviour to which it is appropriate, it is certainly not so to all. Many rituals are performed without any sign of strong emotion, quite casually, though those who do them think them very important. In other cases the theory has the relationship the wrong way round: I don't first feel anxious and then arrange an initiation rite; rather, my

[7] E.g., *Mysticism and Logic* (1918). Religion is an emotional, not a cognitive, response to life.

[8] R. R. Marrett, *The Threshold of Religion* (2nd edn, 1914), p. XXXI.

[9] Thucydides (Book VII, 6) similarly describes how the Athenians on shore gestured in their anguish, as they watched their navy in the last sea battle against the Syracusans, 'their bodies swaying this way and that'.

75

initiation is coming up and I do not relish the prospect of being circumcised with a blunt stone knife!

Malinowski,[10] together with many of the long line of his British followers, was also willing to take something of a sociological view of ritual; even though he rejected the thoroughgoing sociological approach of Emile Durkheim. Malinowski emphasized the essentially public character of religion, and regarded its rituals as a collective social response to crisis. Standard public ritual performances, at times of crisis, bind people together in shared belief, mutual support, and affirmation of the public moral order.[11]

The French anthropologist Lucien Lévy-Bruhl, in a series of books about primitive thought, was the first to bring out adequately the importance of symbolism. His language is cumbrous to our ears, but what he says is that the way primitive man perceives the world is governed by the 'collective representations' of his society, and these collective representations, or common ideas, are in turn determined by what he calls 'the law of mystical participation'. What he means by this difficult idea is best suggested by examples. A man may participate in his shadow, and so regard it as dangerous to walk across an open space when the sun is directly overhead; he may participate in his name, and regard it as very dangerous to reveal it to an enemy; and he may participate in his child, so that when the child is ill, the father drinks the medicine. In short, the world is seen in terms of a network of symbolic affinities and correspondences.[12]

[10] Bronislaw Malinowski (1884-1942) studied several Melanesian peoples, and was Professor of Anthropology at London University, 1927-1942. He was the first great field-worker.

[11] B. Malinowski, 'Magic, Science and Religion', first pub. 1925; reissued in a volume of the same title, London, Souvenir Press 1974.

[12] Useful short account in E. E. Evans-Pritchard, *Theories of Primitive Religion* (O.U.P. 1965), chapter IV. An example from our own society is the much-criticized airline advertisement in which a stewardess says invitingly, 'Fly me'. The 'collective representation' is our common tendency to see vehicles as feminine, and call them 'she'. The stewardess becomes symbolically equivalent to the plane. As the aeroplane encloses the passengers in what the advertisement calls 'wide-bodied comfort', so the stewardess will mother them solicitously. The imagery is maternal, and there is a link of 'mystical participation' between stewardess and aircraft.

The general consensus now is that Lévy-Bruhl made far too much of the distinction between the prelogical, mystical thought of primitives, and our own supposedly purely logical and rational thinking. Indeed the tendency in recent thought has been more and more to recognize that what Lévy-Bruhl says is true of primitives is true of us too. And Lévy-Bruhl was an armchair theorizer, whereas most anthropologists nowadays are basically field-workers.

Nevertheless, the true founder of modern social anthropology, Evans-Pritchard, defended Lévy-Bruhl and got from him a crucial idea for the interpretation of ritual. He puts the point thus: 'Lévy-Bruhl was one of the first, if not the first, to emphasize that primitive ideas, which seem so strange to us ... when considered as isolated facts, are meaningful when considered as parts of patterns of ideas and behaviour, each part having an intelligible relationship to the others. He recognized that values form systems as coherent as the logical constructions of the intellect ...'[13] Here the study of ritual is beginning to be regarded as the royal road to the discovery of the entire world-view of a society. There is, after all, a parallel with Freud's *Interpretation of Dreams.* In the case of dreams you have to analyse the dream-symbolism, the dream-work, and the context of the dream in the patient's life;[14] and similarly in the case of ritual, if you analyse in sufficient detail the symbolism, the dynamics, and the occasions of ritual performances, you will begin to grasp the whole collective world-view which underlies it, and of which individual members of society may be only imperfectly conscious.

Evans-Pritchard also often used the word *Gestalt* in connection with his insistence that in order to understand a particular piece of ritual behaviour you must by patient fieldwork analyse the whole form of life of which it is part, and in terms of which it makes sense. During the last generation the work of many students of African ritual, such as R. G. Lienhardt and V. W. Turner, has followed this method with striking success.

[13] Op. cit., p. 86.
[14] S. Freud, *The Interpretation of Dreams*, Eng. trs., J. Strachey. London, Allen & Unwin 1954 and many others.

I think we may conclude from this that the anthropologists[15] have arrived at a view of ritual action which overlaps considerably with what the theologians say about it. Thus, through the performance of rituals society's world-view is symbolically expressed and reaffirmed, experience is organized, and people are tided over crises in their lives. This is not far from the view expressed by Christian theologians that the performance of a sacrament is a proclamation and enactment of the Gospel, a collective expression of faith. By celebrating the Eucharist, 'you proclaim the Lord's death until he comes'.[16] Again, the ritual action is not simply an individual performance, but an act performed with the whole weight of society and tradition, and indeed the command of God, behind it. It is that vast and collective background that matters, rather than the individual agent's intentions. So theologians say that the sacraments are divinely instituted, and are acts of Christ in the Church, rather than individual performances. The unworthiness of the ministers hinders not the effect of the Sacrament.[17]

The anthropologists began, a century ago, with a number of attitudes to ritual that have gradually been cleared away. There was the old philosophical disparagement of ritual; there was Protestant condemnation of 'ritualism'; there was the view that ritual was primitive and erroneous technology; and there was a Whiggish evolutionism which suggested that savages are childish compared with us. The pioneers viewed societies in terms of models of historical development such as these: savagery-barbarism-civilization; animism-religion-philosophy-science; promiscuity-polygamy-monogamous marriage; collective religion-individual religion; primitive communism-private property; magical childhood thinking-adult logical thinking. These models provided the contrasts in terms of which they understood the differences between 'primitive' men and themselves.

Now we take a somewhat different view. We still make a rough distinction between science and religion, between technical

[15] Not all of them, of course, for many are materialists of one kind or another.
[16] 1 Cor. 11.26.
[17] See No. XXVI of the *Articles of Religion*, which expresses the traditional Western doctrine on this point.

and ritual operations. But both are present, in one way or another, in all societies.[18] Tribal men in a subsistence economy, living by hunting, foodgathering or herding domesticated animals, would not survive at all unless they had a great deal of technical-type knowledge of animals, plants and the weather, and of how to make weapons, boats and the like as efficient as the available tools and materials permit. In that sense every society has science and technology, and Lévy-Bruhl was clearly wrong to talk as if tribal men lived in a magical dream-world.

But if we have been forced to recognize that tribal man is a more practically-minded person than used to be thought, we have also come to see that ritual and symbolic action and thinking play a larger part in our society than was formerly thought. People failed to see this, partly because it is always other people's customs that seem odd and in need of explanation rather than one's own, and partly because in our own large-scale society, which has become so pluralistic, there is such a jostling confusion of different fundamental religious and philosophical outlooks. For much of the time, especially in our public life, we concentrate on overt technical questions (to which agreed solutions seem possible) because we simply do not know how to reach agreement on the deeper underlying questions of our basic world-picture.

An example will make the point clearer. In most 'advanced' or industrialized countries (and, above all, in liberal English-speaking democracies) the dominant ethic in public life is utilitarian. The test of the goodness of a deed lies in its consequences. Pleasure (or happiness or satisfaction or benefit) is the only good, and the equal pleasures of any two persons are equally good. The sole criterion of an action's rightness is its tendency to produce the greatest and most widely-distributed surplus of pleasures over pains. The optimal solution to any practical problem is the one that maximizes benefits and has minimal disadvantages. The phrase 'cost-benefit analysis' well brings out the appeal to technically-minded administrators of such an ethic. For any organization, the administrator's duty is so to order it as to maximize output and minimize unit-cost.

[18] Robin Horton and Ruth Finnegan, eds., *Modes of Thought* (London, Faber & Faber 1973), contains a conspectus of views.

Utilitarianism is impartial and in tendency strongly egalitarian, and its practical application in the welfare state has been a force for good. But it is very noticeable that it is not a complete ethical theory, for it does not (and cannot by itself) decide the question of the *scope* of the moral community. Just *whose* pleasures and pains have to be taken into the reckoning? Should rich countries 'redistribute' their wealth in favour of poor countries? Politically, it is possible as yet to make only very small token gestures in this direction. Still more difficult, are *human embryos* and *animals* among those beings whose welfare, whose pleasures and pains, are of moral significance? Utilitarianism presupposes that we know who belongs to the moral community; but we do not, for we are not agreed where the questions of abortion and cruelty to animals are concerned. English law reflects our uncertainty on these matters. Thus an unborn embryo has some of the rights of a citizen, for a person can (in many countries) sue for compensation for injuries sustained while still in the womb. He claims the *remedy* retrospectively, after live birth, but has the *right* while still *in utero*. And yet, at the same time, abortion law has been getting laxer.[19] And our attitudes towards animals, and the question of their status in law, are even more confused.

I think this illustrates the incompleteness of a purely technical or instrumental attitude to life. Nor can purely scientific knowledge tell us much about the pleasure and pain of (say) amphibians, and whether it is of moral significance,[20] or decide upon purely scientific criteria at what point in its development from conception onwards an embryonic human being shall be accorded the full status of a member of the moral community. Even more convoluted are arguments in the area of conservation, when people try to argue in utilitarian terms (of their value *to*

[19] G. R. Dunstan points out the contradiction here in *The Artifice of Ethics* (London, S.C.M. 1974), p. 80.

[20] In 1974 an English magistrate decided that you cannot be cruel to a frog. See *J. J. C. Smart, 'An Outline of a System of Utilitarian Ethics', in Smart and Bernard Williams, *Utilitarianism: For and Against*. C.U.P. 1973. In his opening pages Smart repeatedly equivocates on whether utilitarian ethics includes animals in the moral community, and also seems to say that the decision one way or the other cannot be justified philosophically, but is non-rational.

man) for the preservation of areas of the environment *untouched
by man*! In the last resort, as well as our purely descriptive
zoology, we need a *ritual zoology*: a religious map of the animal
kingdom which suggests how different animals should be valued
and treated by us, and which relates animals to men in an overall
picture of the created order.

Surprisingly, we already have a ritual zoology. The trouble is
that it is out-of date, and needs rethinking. Here is a map of it,
which I have invented with the help of hints in Claude Lévi-
Strauss. We begin by drawing two axes, one representing the
polarity between Nature (the wild) and Culture (the domesticated), and the other that between the Clean (or edible) and the
Unclean (or inedible).[21] On the resulting grid we plot seven
positions:

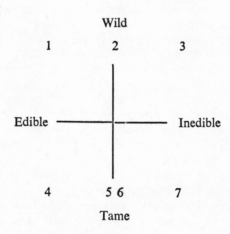

The seven categories of animal are then:

1. *Game*, which is both wild and edible, and may be killed by
shooting.

---

[21] A very much more detailed scheme than mine is set out by E. R.
Leach in an essay in *E. H. Lenneberg, ed., *New Directions in the Study
of Language*. Cambridge, Mass., M.I.T. Press 1964. The reader may
care to consider gardens as expressions of our ritual *botany*, with the
various categories of plants carefully segregated. Why, for example,
are the vegetables hidden round the back?

2. *Ordinary neutral wild creatures*, which are not of economic significance.

3. *Vermin*, the unclean 'criminals' of the animal world, killed by trapping, shooting or poisoning, and often publicly exhibited after they are dead.

4. *Farm animals*, bred for eating, which must be killed 'humanely'.

5. *Working animals*, such as the horse, which may sometimes be eaten, and are killed, like game, by shooting.

6. *Pets*, the most humanized of animals. We don't like to think of their being killed at all, and use euphemisms.

7. *The Fox*, who is vermin, and certainly inedible, yet is also very close to us, and is the subject of many folk-tales and legends. He must be ritually killed.

This is the *ritual zoology* of the English countryman, and it explains why we treat the different kinds of animals as we do. Notice that it is intensely practical and economic, thus rebuking the idea that science and technology are practical, whereas ritual and religious symbolism are somehow fanciful or impractical. Notice too that some of the conflicts in our attitudes to animals arise because they may occupy more than one place in the chart. Rabbits and pigeons, for instance, may be classified under headings 1, 3 and 6, to the confusion of children.

If my 'ritual zoology' guides you in your behaviour towards animals, then you will not see any inconsistency between belonging to the Royal Society for the Prevention of Cruelty to Animals and freely killing animals in classes 3, 4 and 7. Other members of that Society, however, have different ritual zoologies: some are vegetarians, with an ethic of *ahimsā*, non-violence, borrowed from India, which prescribes that no animals shall be killed; and others draw on our modern scientific zoology. Our scientific zoology has, after all, ideas of kinship built into it. The animals that are most intelligent and closest kin to ourselves deserve special consideration. Such people are inclined to give special moral status to mammals, and perhaps birds, and are indignant about the maltreatment of apes in laboratories, over-fished whales and so on. It is clearly necessary to clarify our ritual zoology for the future, if only to reduce the violent conflicts which bedevil the R.S.P.C.A.! Such a clarification must have regard to (i) a general picture, of a religious kind, of man's place in nature and relation to the beasts; (ii) economic facts; and (iii) our modern evolutionary biology.

This example illustrates the way in which scientific knowledge is never quite pure and bare, but in its cultural setting is always wrapped about with what I have called 'ritual': patterns of actions and symbolism which are religious, metaphysical or 'ideological'. This cultural *clothing* of science is easier to see in a historical perspective, and the modern study of the history of science has strongly emphasized it.

Finally, a word about the old topic of the efficacy of prayer. Friedrich Heiler, in the best-known book on the subject, says that 'prayer is at first a spontaneous emotional discharge, a free outpouring of the heart. In the course of development it becomes a fixed formula which people recite without feeling ...'[22] A true Victorian, he regards rituals as merely degenerate prayers. Since his time we have reversed the order, for we now move not from the private realm to the public, but from the public to the private, so that prayers must now be seen as private, inner rituals.

The story is a curious one. Ancient Roman religion was not marked by any great theological refinement or moral seriousness, but the Romans did have a great many rituals, a capacity for making nice distinctions, and a desire to get things just right. So they developed a very rich vocabulary for religious operations, which was inherited by the Western Church. This elaborate technical vocabulary helped make possible the great complexity of Catholic theology. If we add to this the general movement from ceremonial to verbal forms mentioned earlier, we can perceive the enormous range of possible religious speech-acts as being traceable back to what were originally ritual, and indeed ceremonial, acts. Prayers are in fact interiorized ritual actions. Thus a sin-offering for a ritual transgression developed into a public act of penance, and then into auricular confession before a priest, and that in turn into a private 'act' of contrition.

We must conclude that a prayer is not a technical operation, and so it is not appropriate to test its efficacy experimentally

[22] F. Heiler, *Prayer* (O.U.P. 1932), p. 65. The first German edition appeared in 1918.

in the way that one might test a fertilizer or a new drug. A prayer is a particular kind of ritual action, an expression of faith and a way of structuring the self's (or the community's) relation to God, or the gods. The sense in which it works is spelled out in the belief-system of the people who use it. And we have seen that both technology and ritual are always present in one form or another in every society, strangely mingled.

DISCUSSION QUESTIONS

What is ritual action? Is it *rational*? Examine ritual in our own culture, for example, in connection with dress, eating, and marriage customs. How far do these rituals express a coherent view of the world and of society? Examine one or more religious rituals, for example, a communion service, and ask what beliefs are expressed in the way the rite is done.

A man lay dreaming, and in his dream a bullock appeared to him and said, 'If there were another species which stood to you in the same relation as you stand to cattle, you would not grant it the right to eat you. So why do you eat us?' When he woke, the man resolved to be a vegetarian. Is the bullock's argument sound? What cosmological considerations arise, in replying to the bullock, concerning man's place in nature, relation to animals, etc.?

7

OBJECTIVE KNOWLEDGE

A large collection of illustrated books, mostly of the eighteenth and nineteenth centuries, has just been presented to my College. Among its thousands of volumes are most of the old classics of travel, topography and natural history, including the first great floras and bird-books. The fine hairspring line of the engraver is particularly suited to insects and grasses, and many of these early drawings have never been bettered.

It occurs to me that if one of the great men of the past, whom I have to spend a good deal of time studying, were to leap off the page and demand, 'Well, what has your age to show for itself?', I might produce something like this for him. It would be vulgar and silly to try to astonish such a man with our technological gewgaws, but I think he would be full of admiration for a modern bird-book. For the price of only about two hours of a working man's labour you can obtain in any book-shop a compendium which, exhaustively and with a very high degree of accuracy, describes and classifies every species of European bird, and gives distribution-maps. Behind such a book there are plainly many lifetimes of collective effort in close and systematic observation, and nothing like it existed before the modern period. Aristotle is reckoned to mention some 500 species of animal, which is a great achievement in relation to the knowledge of his time, and he was the first true zoologist. Medieval carvers showed, for example, in the capitals at Southwell Minster, a very exact observation of foliage. Artists like Leonardo and Dürer produced fine biological drawings. But all this is trivial compared with the quality of work in natural history which was available in cheap books by the late nineteenth century.

Perhaps still more striking is the level of exact knowledge of exotic peoples and cultures which has been attained in the last century. A standard work like E. E. Evans-Pritchard's *Nuer Religion* (O.U.P. 1956) could not have been written in earlier times. Travellers' tales about the odd customs of people in foreign parts have been told at least since Herodotus (480–425 B.C.), but such material was crude in the extreme compared with what is available now. Nowhere before the late nineteenth century did anyone have an accurate and sympathetic understanding of alien cultures, religions or artistic traditions.[1]

Without multiplying examples, we can surely agree that modern man has an objective knowledge of the world about him to an extent previously unknown, and that the 'objectivity' here has something to do with scientific method. Exact and systematic observation, careful measurement, the performance of experiments and the interpretation of the data obtained, the formulation and rigorous testing of hypotheses—all this has created an immense body of knowledge of a kind that did not exist before. There were forerunners, but nothing on this scale.

What is more, the development of an immense body of objective knowledge of the world about us in modern times seems directly connected with the decline of religion. The difference between a medieval bestiary[2] and a modern work of zoology is that symbolic and religious ways of looking at animals have been replaced by cool and intense observation of natural fact.

Similarly, in the early Middle Ages, maps of the Earth were determined by symbolic and religious considerations. A monk would draw the main land-mass of the Old World in a T- or Cross-shape, putting Jerusalem (and its symbolic counterpart, Eden) at the centre. Such maps expressed a religious vision of the Earth, and owed almost nothing to direct observation and measurement. Contrast the procedure employed when the Ordnance Survey of Great Britain began in the late eighteenth century. This time the mapping was done by triangulation. Landmarks were selected as triangulation-points, and theodolites

[1] See the (frankly) disgraceful accounts of Hinduism in Jules Verne's *Round the World in Eighty Days* (1872), and Wilkie Collins' *The Moonstone* (1868), and then see how much better are Kipling and E. M. Forster.

[2] See T. H. White, *The Book of Beasts*. London, Jonathan Cape 1954.

were set up on top of them. From the trig-point the angles between all the other visible landmarks were carefully measured. When this had been done for all the trig-points in an area, it was a simple exercise in geometry to connect up the lines and so obtain an exact mathematical representation of the relative positions of all the selected points. By an extension of the same technique the details could be filled in, too.

The modern procedure is geometrical, and non-religious. Nothing is located absolutely, or religiously. The world is seen as a system of interconnected *human* view-points. It is a relativistic vision of the world, but the exact measurement of the relations, and their systematic interconnection, produces a kind of web or net on which everything is plotted with a high degree of accuracy.

We glimpse here an intriguing parable of the nature of modern knowledge, and it is worth following it up, because it reveals the character of modern objectivity.

Ancient prose romance or historical narrative tells us little or nothing about the inner lives, or personal view-point, of the characters involved. The story is told from an absolute or 'God's-eye' view, because, in a theistic universe, plot is providence. The objectivity is religious. In *Beowulf* or *The Battle of Maldon* there is no trace of consideration of the events as from the human point of view of one of the actors in the story. It can occasionally happen in medieval romance that as the hero arrives at a castle in the evening, or wanders through a forest, or sets out on a new quest, we momentarily glimpse the scene before him as it looks to him. But we do not enter the inner life of the characters, or learn that the story is a *different story* as seen from different personal viewpoints within it. We do not find any suggestion that different people see different worlds. There is only the absolute world-view, and the storyline itself is highly objective.

It is only about the time of *Sir Gawain and the Green Knight* and Chaucer that the-world-as-it-appears-to-the-individual enters literature, at about the same time as perspective enters art.

Perspective is a very paradoxical topic. Geometry is *a priori* and universal, and yet, for men to grasp the geometrical structure of space, it was necessary to examine how the world *appears*

87

from a *point* within it. Artists, learning perspective, shut one eye and laid the other close to the point of a spike. They looked over this sighting-point through a strung-frame grid at the subject to be painted, and copied what they saw square by square. Painting without perspective is painting from a God's-eye view. But painting the world as it appears from a finite point-of-view discloses the geometry of space; especially when the same object is painted from several different viewpoints, and then the mind uses these various representations to synthesize a picture of the spatially-extended object.

The ancient philosophical distinction between appearance and reality now takes on a new form. *My* perspective on the world is appearance, *ours* is reality. To return to mapping by triangulation, if I am alone on one trig-point, I see only the landscape as it appears to me, and have no chance of producing an accurate map of it. But if there are other people standing with instruments on top of other landmarks within my view, then the group of us, by co-ordinating our observations, can produce a highly-accurate map of the area around us.

It was not easy to grasp the idea of perspective, because our vision of the world is so intellectual. We do not naturally see the world geometrically as from a point. Hold up your right hand two feet before your eyes, and your left hand one foot before your eyes; and then look at your two hands—and you will see that the right hand appears to be, not half the size of the left, but nearly the same size.[3] Because we are mobile, we see stereoscopically, and we unconsciously interpret what we see, it was necessary to make a deliberate effort to discover what the world looks like to a stationary, one-eyed, disciplined point-observer. The idea influenced painting, literature and science, and was very powerful. The example of mapping suggests how a community of observers, collating their results, can build up a novel and geometrically-accurate representation of the world.

This helps to show why scientific work is so strongly communal. You can be an isolated poet, but not an isolated scientist. And the idea of the world as a system of points of view greatly influenced philosophers such as Leibniz, Berkeley and John

[3] But close one eye, and your right hand shrinks.

Stuart Mill. Einstein's vision of nature was not such a startling innovation as some have thought.

A difficult philosophical question arises here: do we still need God? The contrast that has come to be made is one between my private and subjective point of view and our (that is, society's) common, public and objective world-view. The public world, in much modern thought, can be adequately portrayed as a co-ordinated system of private viewpoints. However, Leibniz and Berkeley still thought God's absolute knowledge of the world necessary to complete the system. So, perhaps, did Einstein. The world of nature cannot be completely determined by point-observers within it, but needs the absolute view of an infinite observer outside space and time, to save determinism. God ordains the whole system, and the co-ordination of the appearances, so assuring us that *our* world is *the* world.

A further complication is this: are we thinking of *abstract* or *concrete* observers? The philosopher George Berkeley (1685–1753) was a rebel against the natural philosophy of Newton and Locke. In effect, he said that the world of science is a hypothetical world as it might appear to an *abstract* or theoretical observer. With its absolute space and time, and its colourless, odourless and noiseless particles shooting about in accordance with mathematical laws, it is not the world actual people can see with the senses they actually have. Berkeley did not deny any of Newton's science *as science*; what he objected to was the popular notion that the hypothetical world of physics was the *real* world, whereas the world of sense-experience was somehow illusory. Instead, Berkeley insisted that the world of sense is the primary reality, and the world of physics merely a useful abstraction from it. So in his own philosophy Berkeley insisted on the logical and religious primacy of the concrete human observer who sees colours, hears noises, feels hot or cold, and so on. In Berkeley's universe there are only two sorts of real thing, perceivers (which he calls 'spirits', i.e., men, and God, the absolute perceiver) and things-perceived (which he calls, somewhat misleadingly, 'ideas').

In what sense, then, can physical theory be called 'objectively' true? Take the Newtonian concepts of absolute space and motion, matter, force, gravity and so on. These concepts are not 'real essences', representing a *real* world behind the world of appearance. That is the mistake of 'essentialism'. Rather, they are mathematical hypotheses, calculating devices for the prediction of appearances. Science does not discover the hidden nature of things, or describe a more real world behind the world of sense. Scientific explanation is hypothetical, or conjectural. That does not mean that it is arbitrary; on the contrary, one physical theory may be a closer approximation to the truth than another. Science does aim at truth, even though it must never pretend to possess absolute truth. It proposes a model of nature. That model is not the reality, but only an approximation, a hypothesis useful so far as it successfully co-ordinates the data, but perpetually open to revision or even replacement.[4]

The typical modern philosophy of science, then, of which Berkeley is an important forerunner, is cautious in its claims. Scientific knowledge is objective, not because it literally uncovers the hidden essences of things, but in a much more austere sense. It is objective insofar as it survives attempts to falsify it, successfully explains the data, generates predictions which are fulfilled, and yet remains always open to correction; and its claim to be objective is supported by the assertion that nothing better is possible. It is objective *because* it is provisional, and because other presumptive or alleged kinds of knowledge do not come anywhere near to its high standards of intellectual virtue. There is one exception, for Sir Karl Popper himself insists that we do have knowledge of the *a priori* world, the world of logic and mathematics, which is independent of experience. So there is the world of sense-experience, there is the hypothetical world of physical theory, and there is the world of pure thought, of logic and mathematics. Who is going to venture to claim that in the realms of morality, art and religion knowledge is attainable whose objectivity is definable and defensible according to the high standards set by the logician and the physicist?

A scientist of distinction who is willing to spell out the implications of an austerely and exclusively scientific ideal of

[4] See George Berkeley's notebooks, the *Philosophical Commentaries*, in A. A. Luce and T. E. Jessop, eds., *The Works of George Berkeley*, Vol. I. London, Nelson 1948; and the *De Motu* (1721), discussed by Karl Popper in 'A Note on Berkeley as Precursor of Mach and Einstein', in C. B. Martin and D. M. Armstrong, *Locke and Berkeley*. London, Macmillan.

objective knowledge is Jacques Monod, in his book, *Chance and Necessity*,[5] one of the latest and best of its kind.

Monod takes his stand on 'the principle of objectivity', which, for him, asserts that *only* scientific knowledge counts as objective knowledge. I have tried in the preceding pages to give as strong an interpretation as I can of this claim. There are three main sorts of scientific knowledge—descriptive, theoretical and technical. Technical knowledge is simply applied science, the skill of controlling nature, and it raises ethical questions rather than questions of doctrine or metaphysics. Theoretical scientific knowledge we have just discussed. Descriptive scientific knowledge is the natural-history type of knowledge from which we began, and which I believe is much underrated.

These three kinds of knowledge are different. When Monod says 'only scientific knowledge is objective knowledge', he can defend his claim by pointing to (i) our growing technical control over nature; (ii) the growing explanatory power of our scientific theory; and (iii) the descriptive detail and accuracy of our natural-history maps of the organic and inorganic worlds about us.

He fails to do this, but he should have done it. Instead he produces a kind of evolutionary historicism. To survive, man must understand and control the world about him, but he can learn to do this only in collaboration with other men. Certain insects—ants, bees, wasps and termites—have become social, but their social behaviour is genetically-determined, and 'automatic'. Man needs to live in society, but without becoming an automaton. So in man, society's authority is a matter of culture, rather than genetics. Religions, philosophies, moralities, and ideologies are culturally-created instruments for maintaining social cohesion. They all presuppose the 'animist' illusion, that there is some superhuman purpose in the world by which human society is bound together, rooted in the cosmic order, and swept forward to its destiny. All religions, and Marxism too, are animistic, for they all unite fact and value, proposing an explanation of the world which is also a justification of morality and of society's authority. So deep is our need for such an

⁵ Paris: Éditions du Seuil 1970; Eng. tr., London, Collins 1972; paperback edn 1974.

'animistic' faith that Monod suggests it has become genetically inbuilt.

Modern science began in Christendom, Monod suggests, because of the Church's distinction between the sacred and the profane (see my comment to much the same effect above, p. 20). Since all value was grounded in the sacred, the distinction suggested the possibility of a value-free and autonomous pursuit of knowledge in the profane realm. Since questions of personal faith and commitment belonged to the sacred realm, an impartial and dispassionate attitude seemed appropriate to the profane. Thus knowledge was separated from value.

Now a paradox arises. Scientific enquiry is itself a form of action, and all action presupposes values. Monod calls the moral postulate presupposed by scientific activity, the 'ethic of knowledge'. By definition the ethic of knowledge cannot be justified, for animism of every kind has been rejected. It is simply chosen, or laid upon himself, by the scientist. The free choice of the ethic of knowledge proves man's freedom; the self-knowledge of himself as biological being that it makes possible proves his capacity for transcendence, and it alone gives him courage to face the unfeeling immensity of the universe, out of which he emerged only by chance. Monod argues that there might be a workable socialism-without-illusions, based on the ethic of knowledge.

Monod's romantic conclusion recalls the somewhat similar sentiments of Freud[6] and Russell.[7] But how sound is his argument? There are real questions about whether discoveries in molecular biology can have the comprehensive philosophical implications that he claims for them. After all, that our existence owes much to 'chance' has been recognized for as long as men have understood the facts of sexual reproduction, for our parents did not *select* the spermatozöon and the ovum from whose union we have sprung. They left it to 'chance'. And that ideas of an immanent purpose are not required in biological explanation, even if true, does nothing to prove that they can never be rightly applied in some other context. The painting on my wall is made of nothing but chemicals, and ideas of purpose play no part in

[6] E.g., *New Introductory Lectures on Psychoanalysis* (London, Hogarth Press 1923), Lecture 35.
[7] 'A Free Man's Worship', in *Mysticism and Logic*. 1918.

chemistry, but I can still examine the painting and conclude that the artist intended it to portray a bearded man of about fifty years in a ruff and a fur-trimmed cloak. And, since the ethic of knowledge is adopted by a purely arbitrary decision as the presupposition of scientific enquiry, we cannot exclude the possibility that on the basis of another decision another and more adequate and complete world-view than Monod's own might be arrived at.[8]

A question of very general importance now arises. Monod gives a broad sketch of the evolutionary development of the human brain. Can such an account ever explain how it itself is possible? That is, can we give a scientific account of the human brain which will explain how this remarkable organ is able to give a scientific account of itself? (And then we might ask how it can explain its own ability to understand its own explanation of how it can give a scientific account of itself, and so on.)

Monod tries bravely, and sees the pitfalls. Just because he insists on man's power of self-transcendence through objective knowledge, he recognizes that the mind is mysterious, and cannot easily be identified with the brain, at least in the present state of our knowledge.

Study of the functions of the brain is a growth-point in science now, and the desire for continuity in scientific explanation is so strong that a great many professionals in the field are very strongly inclined to identify mental events with electro-chemical events in the brain. A few philosophers support them, but here is a repellent illustration of the difficulty of doing so.

Suppose that when I see something, my-seeing-it is to be identified with the occurrence of certain physical processes in my cerebral cortex. Suppose that a square inch of my skull is removed so as to expose that part of my cerebral cortex. Suppose further that, with a little gentle dissection, a powerful microscope, and minute electrodes, 'my-seeing-something' could actually be exposed, and watched occurring. Now, with the help of prisms let us bend the microscope round, so that I can look

---

[8] See Mary Hesse, 'On the Alleged Incompatibility between Christianity and Science', in H. W. Montefiore, ed., *Man and Nature*. London, Collins 1975.

through the eye-piece at the exposed bit of my own brain. All this may be technically difficult, but it is not logically impossible (i.e., there is no self-contradiction in the supposition that with the help of mirrors or prisms I could observe my own brain). Now, on the materialist supposition, the thing observed, and the observing of it are identical; and the more we think about this hypothetical situation the more full of paradoxes it seems, and the more impossible is the materialist account of the mind. How can a physical event *be* its own watching of itself occurring?

Monod, as we have seen, admits the mysteriousness of the mind, but the pull of the idea of continuity is strong, and he still feels that the evolution of the brain must throw light on the nature of mind. Indeed, he goes so far as to say that 'objective analysis obliges us to see that this seeming duality (of brain and spirit) ... is an illusion'. He does not say what the objective analysis in question is, but merely points to the compelling reasons why we must for the present persist in the 'illusion'.

Monod lists five functions of the central nervous system: (i) it controls motor activity, especially in response to sensory input; (ii) it contains genetically-innate programmes of action to be triggered by appropriate stimuli; (iii) it analyses sensory inputs to construct an action-guiding model of the external world; (iv) it registers and classifies events and, where appropriate, modifies its programmes accordingly; and (v) it *imagines* or simulates possible future events and programmes of action.

Of these five functions (i)-(iii) are co-ordinative and representational. They can be confidently attributed to insects. (iv) and (v) are cognitive, and may be able to create subjective experience. (iv) can be attributed (on the basis of J. Z. Young's famous work) to the octopus. (v) may belong to mammals only, for in their case at least we can be pretty certain that they dream, and that dreaming is in them much the same as it is in us.

The crucial fact about the human brain is the enormous development of function (v), the power of imagination or simulation by which man can generate new thought-structures and programmes of action, and transmit them culturally. Monod thinks he can solve the old philosophical argument between rationalists and empiricists. The empiricists derived all mental

94

functions from experience. The rationalists (thinkers like Descartes and Kant) held that the basic truths of logic and mathematics—our *a priori* knowledge—cannot be derived from experience, but must be regarded as 'innate'. The word 'innate' is metaphorical. The essential point is that the logical, interpretative and constructive powers of the mind are always *presupposed by* our objective knowledge of the world about us, and therefore cannot be regarded as *products* of it.

Monod's solution is that the *a priori* has become genetically inbuilt during the long course of cultural evolution. But this fails, for it makes the *a priori* merely the *a posteriori* at one remove. What our ancestors learnt by experience, has become in us a genetic datum. Such a causal account of how we seem to ourselves to have *a priori* knowledge does nothing to explain its peculiar intellectual authority. After all, Monod himself says that the 'animistic' or religious demand for a total teleological explanation of the universe and man's place in it has *also* become genetically inbuilt, though he regards this latter as invalid. So genetic inbuiltness and biological utility are *not* the same as validity.

In summary, Monod has not proved that scientific knowledge is the only objective knowledge. He has not proved that mental events are identical with physical brain-processes; and, what is more, scientific knowledge itself presupposes *a priori* knowledge, so you cannot give a complete scientific account of *a priori* knowledge. The Greeks, with their special interest in logic and mathematics, were the first people who were deeply struck by the miracle of *a priori* knowledge, and ever since Plato a line of philosophers have regarded it as making impossible a purely naturalistic account of man. He is not only a product of natural 'Chance and Necessity'; he has access to a supernatural world—he is an immortal soul. These last phrases may seem too portentous, and too rich in overtones, but I mean by them merely what Pascal has said in his *Pensées*: [9] 'Man is but a reed, the weakest in nature; but he is a thinking reed ... if the Universe were to crush him, man would still be nobler than his

[9] Penguin edition (1961), nos. 254ff. The order Pascal intended for his *Pensées* is uncertain, and different editions number them in different ways.

killer. For he knows that he is dying, and that the Universe has the advantage over him; the Universe knows nothing of this'.[10] There is that in the mind which is *not* just a product of nature: if there were not, we could not know nature. Indeed, since later antiquity *a priori* truth has been regarded by many rationalist and idealist philosophers as the very structure of the divine intellect, and man's aptitude for it as a proof that he is made by God for God. Modern thought about religion is so often wayward and irrational that it is worth recalling that for many great thinkers of the past the most God-revealing books were books of logic and mathematics.

What, then are the differences between scientific and religious ideas of objectivity? The issue is not a simple one, and there is a wide range of points of view. Some liberals, such as the Cambridge philosopher F. R. Tennant, and more recently Dr A. R. Peacocke,[11] emphasize the similarities. In both religion and science we find a communal quest for truth; in both a kind of humility is required; in both there is the appeal to experience; and in both models or analogies are proposed even though their inadequacy is recognized. In the Puritan tradition that stems from Calvin and Karl Barth there is emphasis both on the autonomy of natural science and on the objective givenness of revelation. Theology is objective insofar as it is done in a spirit of humility and obedience to revelation. The tradition that stems from Kant and existentialists, by contrast, strongly contrasts the objective, impersonal and value-neutral character of science with the intensely ethical, subjective and self-involving religious attitude.

These last two views are particularly important, for they are not just symptoms of, they seek to *justify*, a deep split in our culture which goes right back to the old issue of faith and reason.

[10] Compare the fine image at the end of chapter 8 of John Cowper Powys' *Wolf Solent* (London, Jonathan Cape 1929), where Solent, walking along a country lane at night, sees an old woman reading by candle-light in a remote cottage. The candlelight in the vast surrounding darkness becomes an image of human consciousness in the universe.

[11] *Science and the Christian Experiment.* O.U.P. 1971.

DISCUSSION QUESTIONS

Can the 'scientific outlook' as described by Freud, C. H. Waddington, Monod and many others, be a sufficient basis for social life? If it is deficient, in what does its deficiency lie?

Sir Karl Popper and others define the 'objective knowledge' yielded by the scientific method in cautious terms. Scientific theories are conjectures-not-yet-refuted. Can it be claimed that another and stronger kind of knowledge is attainable in the fields of personal relationships and morality?

8

SCIENCE AND SOCIETY

For seven centuries Europeans have seen the question of secular and sacred knowledge in dualistic terms. Simply to set out some of the main views is to see the history of Western thought in miniature.

1. Thomas Aquinas (1225–74) made a clear distinction between natural, unassisted human reason and supernatural, divinely-inspired faith, assenting to divine revelation. There was no *contradiction* between the realms of reason and faith, but there was a clear *distinction*, and it ran right through Aquinas' system, marking off nature from grace, State from Church, and the natural moral law which directs man to his temporal (this-worldly) end from the positive divine law which directs him to his eternal destiny.

2. William of Ockham (*c*.1300–49) took the distinction between faith and reason much further. He removed God, the soul, and universals from the realm of what was knowable by reason. Reason itself he understood very parsimoniously: it recognized particulars, and classified them by means of concepts. Correspondingly, Ockham tended to remove the rational element from faith, seeing it almost as pure obedience to the divine will. He thus saw sacred knowledge and secular knowledge as being quite different in kind: the 'double truth'.

3. The Protestants, and among them the followers of John Calvin (1509–64), inherited this dualism between reason and faith. All religious knowledge was founded on scripture (and man's response to its message) alone, and the world of nature was therefore secularized. The old symbolic, animistic and sometimes magical attitudes to nature were expunged. Scripture-guided man ruled over a secularized, bare nature. Here is the background to Sir Francis Bacon (1561–1626): divinity is obedi-

98

ence to scripture, science is the patient attention of natural reason to the detail of nature.

4. The great seventeenth-century thinkers distinguished the two provinces in many different ways. For René Descartes (1596–1650) the main distinction was that between Thought and Extension, between pure reason and the natural world of geometrical matter-in-motion. For Isaac Newton (1642–1727) it was that between mathematical philosophy and sacred history. But, by general agreement, 'the intellectual world was divided into two provinces, as Pope Alexander VI had divided the terrestrial globe'.[1] Nature and the animals were handed over to mechanistic science, while God and the soul and all the ultimates rested with philosophers and divines. (Notice that this partitioning separates man from beast, so helping to explain the shock caused by Darwin. And from Montaigne (1533–92) onwards, animals worry the philosophers.)

5. Immanuel Kant (1724–1804) was still a firm dualist, sharply dividing the 'phenomenal' world of nature from the realm of morality, the 'noumenal' world, apprehended only by pure moral faith. Kant's main concern was to provide a satisfactory rationale for Newtonian physics, while yet preserving human moral freedom and the metaphysical realities presupposed by it.

Since Kant a whole range of opinions has been held, but dualism (as we noticed in Chapter 1, when distinguishing between the magic world and the world of fact) reached its most extreme form in Victorian culture. The masculine public world of industry and commerce was harsh and strenuous; the feminine private world of the home and the imagination was a languorous Christian fairyland. Men were beasts and women were angels. Money made out of mass-production factories was spent on neo-medieval religion, art and architecture. It was a Platonic age, which separated the world of hard fact from the world of ideals.

Even now we have not wholly escaped from the Victorian world-view, which perhaps suggests why so many writers have wanted to claim, on the one hand that the scientific and the religious outlooks are very different, and on the other that

[1] A. R. Hall, *From Galileo to Newton* (London, Collins edn of 1970), p. 347.

they are nevertheless compatible. But we are now far enough away from the Victorians to see that their art and religion were a failure, and that the trouble with the compatibility-thesis is that it does not recognize how far the long tradition of dualism, with its separation of the world of fact from the world of value, has weakened Christian cosmology. In prescientific culture the cosmology, or overall world-picture, validated the social institutions and the moral order, and assigned their place in the universe to the individual and to society. But by Bacon's time, scripture had been separated from nature, and sacred knowledge from factual knowledge, in a way which bodes ill for the future.

As we have seen, what I call 'cosmology', Monod calls 'animism', and, in his own terms, Monod sets out the dilemma very well. It was the separation of value from knowledge, as Monod puts it, which destroyed Christianity and made science possible. The long-term outcome is that modern man can no longer perceive in the cosmos an objective foundation for the moral order, nor a purposive movement which explains how he came to be and promises him his destiny, so that he is spiritually in a very poor condition indeed.

The charge against the compatibility-thesis is, then, that it does not take the question of *cosmology* sufficiently seriously, and so pretends that our religious situation is better than it is.

In reply, it might be said that I am overestimating the role of cosmology in religion. It is perfectly true that in Milton and Dante, in Chaucer and Aquinas, the old Christian cosmology is very conspicuous. But it is easy to find, in the Christian period, mystical writers for whom cosmology does not matter very much at all. If one studies people like Meister Eckhart, or Julian, or St John of the Cross, one can surely say that there is little of importance to them, in their religious life, which is in the slightest affected by the development of modern science.[2]

That is true. An authentic mystical life is possible under almost any cultural conditions. But then, true mystics are rare and highly introverted persons who (for good reasons of their own)

[2] There are also a few major Christian thinkers who do not share the common Christian cosmology, such as Cardinal Nicholas of Cusa, *De Docta Ignorantia* (1440).

do not enter many cognitive claims in the public domain. But *society's* need for a cosmology is much greater than the mystic's. And there remains an important sense in which science has long since destroyed religion. Although in science-based industrial societies a great many individuals have a private religious faith (what Marx calls 'religiosity', when he is writing about the U.S.A.), religion as a public fact is vestigial or extinct.

So it is not surprising that the question has often been asked, how far can 'the scientific outlook' take over the social functions historically performed by religion? We have heard something of Jacques Monod's answer to this question. Freud's is worth considering as well.[3]

For Freud, psychoanalysis is a courageous extension of the scientific outlook into man's inner life and his self-understanding. It demands stringent honesty and freedom from illusions. It recognizes that religion has in the past played a vital part in helping men to bear the burden of emotional frustration that is the price of civilization, but it also recognizes that religion is an illusion. Religion is a projection of the situation of our earliest childhood; the adult human, alone in an indifferent and often cruel universe, still seeks comfort by imagining that he is the child of a heavenly creator-father. He hopes that he can make his way in life by learning to understand and to please this heavenly father, just as in the little world of infancy he learnt to understand and to please his earthly father. But, says Freud, science has overthrown the religious world-view. How far, then, can a scientific world-view replace religion?

Freud answers this question under three headings.

(i) In the first place the myths and doctrines of religion give what is claimed to be information about the origin of the universe, and so (like science) religion sets out to satisfy a fundamental cognitive need. Psychologically, of course, the creator-god is a projection of the believer's own father; that is why he finds the explanation so satisfying. But nowadays science has developed an alternative cosmology which (on the cognitive side, at least, if not on the emotional) is very much better and stronger.

(ii) Secondly, religion promises guidance, protection and final happiness. In this consolatory role, science cannot compete.

[3] *New Introductory Lectures,* 35.

Psychologically, religion exploits the fact that we still demand parental care and reassurance in adult life. But experience of the harshness of life must convince us at last that divine protection is an illusion. If science cannot console, at least it gives us the cold comfort of freedom from illusion.

(iii) Thirdly, religion guides human thought and action by authoritative precepts. Religion offers an affective or emotional basis for morality, which is the same in structure as the parental guidance of children by rewards and punishments. And as a child begs its parents, so in prayer men seek to influence the divine will. But nowadays ethics has lost its foundation in religion, and it is necessary to change over from an emotionally-based religious ethic to a rationally-based and adult scientific ethic. We will be the better for the change.

Freud's position, then, is complicated. He is quite sure that religion is untrue; its doctrines are products of an infantile and primitive attitude to the world, its consolations are untrustworthy, and the foundation it gives to morality is unsound. But he is not like an Enlightenment unbeliever, who thought that religion could simply vanish, leaving nothing behind it but a sigh of relief. Religious beliefs meet deep psychological needs, and cannot be renounced without pain. Nevertheless, they must be abandoned. But the scientific world-view which is to replace them is 'essentially negative'; it emphasizes the reality-principle, and the laborious pursuit of truth, and it refuses illusions. Just as Monod talks cautiously of the possibility of a scientific socialism-without-illusions, so Freud can just envisage a 'dictatorship of reason', a religion of science. But each admits that the mass of men will not easily be satisfied with so bleak a creed.

And there is a rich irony in the position of both men.[4] Freud criticizes the way religion takes infantile experience as the model for understanding man's place in the universe. This is illusion. But in his own arguments, Freud does the same. Primitive men are to modern men as children are to adults; religion is to science as childhood is to adulthood; and we must now abandon religion for the same sort of reasons as we must abandon the comforts of childhood and go out to face the rigours of the adult world.

[4] I suspect Monod is indebted to Freud, and like him compares individual with racial history.

Just like the religious man he criticizes, Freud himself is using one of the oldest of all religious metaphors, the development of the child, in order to understand man's situation in the universe. Paul had used it too, in saying that the Mosaic Law was to the Gospel as childhood to adulthood.

To show the richness and ambiguity of religious metaphors, we can easily reply to Freud on his own terms, and argue that the trust we place in science and technology in modern culture is illusory, being nothing but a projection of infantile belief in the omnipotence of wishes. Modern man's mental age is about seven; he wants his toy-cupboard full of marvellous gadgets, and believes he will be perfectly happy when his environment responds to his every whim. But modern man's gadgets, his greater knowledge, and his technical control over nature have done nothing whatever to alter or diminish the fundamental facts of life, namely, moral evil, suffering, solitude and death. It is time to outgrow utopian fantasies of omniscience and omnipotence, and recognize that we cannot attain final happiness until we come to terms with realities we cannot manipulate. If we read the life of Jesus, or of the Buddha, we may begin to grow up. Science is to religion as infancy to adulthood.

Now, keeping strictly within the thought-world of psychoanalysis, this use of the metaphor of outgrowing childhood is surely just as plausible as Freud's, though it suggests a conclusion directly contrary to his. Freud himself is so carried away by his own self-image as a hard-headed man of science that he barely sees that he is thinking in metaphorical terms at all. Still less does he recognize the looseness and fluidity of such metaphorical thinking. At this point, C. G. Jung comes out well in comparison with Freud, because he is more consistent. Freud is hard and clear on the surface, but deep down he is diffuse and mythological; Jung is diffuse and mythological both on the surface and deep down! But at least Jung openly recognizes that we cannot but seek symbolic correspondences between the life-experience of the individual and the cosmos as a whole.

Still, Freud and Monod are right in saying that the modern scientific world-picture declines to supply the symbolic parallels we seek, because the basic premiss of modern science was a repudiation of precisely such ways of thinking. The picture of the universe drawn by a modern theoretical astronomer *systematically and in principle* refuses to tell us why we are here, how we are to live, and what we should hope for. It follows that such questionings must either be renounced altogether, or seek their answers from somewhere else than science.

Men have not found this lesson easy to learn. Indeed, ever since Galileo they have been trying to make science into religion, or to extract from the scientific representation of the universe the form of an ideal society. So Thomas Hobbes (1588–1679) was already in the 1640s trying to extract from mechanistic physics his psychology and his politics. We have already mentioned Social Darwinism and evolutionary ethics in other contexts. But the most thoroughgoing examples are the anarchist dreams of French revolutionary thinkers. Charles Fourier (1772–1837), for example, modelled the human way of life in his 'Phalansteries' on the motions of the planets.[5] Phalansteries were communes, rather like kibbutzim, but more formally and hierarchically organized and 'omnigamous', dedicated to free love. Universal sexual attraction in the moral realm is the counterpart of universal gravitational attraction in the physical realm. Joseph Dejacque, whose ideas were put forward in the French émigré anarchist paper, *Le Libertaire* (New York, 1858–61), foretold that after centuries of violent struggle against the existing social order, humanity would come to be organized into 'Humanispheres', vast star-shaped buildings.[6]

Fourier and Dejacque are only two examples of a common dream during the Newtonian era, that Newton's model of the solar system could somehow provide the pattern for an ideal human society, just as Bronze Age cities copied the shapes of constellations. Newton's own Puritan segregation of natural philosophy from divinity was a way of saying this was impossible,

[5] Fourier's *Le Nouveau Monde Amoureux* was not published till 1967. Short account of him in John Cairncross, *After Polygamy was made a Sin* (London, Routledge 1974), pp. 203-10. A selection of his writings has been published by Jonathan Cape, London.

[6] George Woodcock, *Anarchism* (U.S. edn World Publishing Company 1962; Penguin edn 1963), pp. 263-6, has a brief account. There is a very long French tradition of elaborating a Newtonian mechanics of the passions.

and more recently the point has been made by saying that scientific models are abstracted and hypothetical. They are not *attempting* to be concrete, authoritative and action-guiding in the way that religious imagery is. It is, after all, simply the case (i) that modern science has destroyed the old public, objective and cosmological kind of religion; and (ii) that it cannot of itself be a satisfactory replacement for it.

It does not follow, however, that no religious belief is possible in scientific culture. Individualized, protestant religion, based on a positive revelation given in scripture, has flourished in the modern period under such names as puritanism, methodism, evangelicalism and Christian existentialism. And as we have said, mystical religion is possible in almost any cultural context.

However, we are at this point brought up against the Marxist critique of religion. Marxism makes a very clear distinction between the grand old public and cosmological type of religion which flourished in primitive society, slave society and feudal society, and the privatized religiosity which may flourish in capitalist society and persist for a long time even in socialist society. To say that religion is tolerated in socialist countries is rather misleading. What has happened is that objective and public religion has been wholly extirpated, and private religiosity is permitted to survive merely because (from the Marxists' very 'public' point of view) it is quite insignificant.

When we put it like that, we can see clearly that the same has happened in Western countries, too. In them also the permitted continuance of some vestiges of the old public reality of religion cannot disguise the fact that public religion no longer exists as an effective force. And though a surprising amount of private religiosity (often of an exceedingly arbitrary and subjective kind) still survives, it is, for all practical purposes, of very minor significance.[7]

The reason why it is insignificant is that private religion needs, and must presuppose, a public dimension if it is to have any

[7] As sociological studies show, it is no longer able even to sustain personal morality. See, for example, Urie Bronfenbrenner's study *Two Worlds of Childhood: U.S. and U.S.S.R.* (London, Allen and Unwin 1971), which vividly illustrates the moral decline of the West, by contrasting it with the U.S.S.R.

effect in the world. Thus, in a survey reported in the Catholic journal *The Month* (December 1974), it was found that almost two-thirds of a sample of one hundred student teachers had enjoyed something like mystical experiences (even though the proportion of practising believers among them was no higher than among the general population).[8] This is a very high figure, but it has to be qualified by the observation that most of the subjects were very unsure what to make of their experiences, had no clear language in which to describe them, and were rather shamefaced about admitting to them. The available public language, present-day English, does not have the resources to allow such experiences to be cognitive, and to be put to publicly-effective use. The lesson here is that, except perhaps in the case of a few very tough-minded individuals, as religion gets squeezed out of the public realm it becomes less and less effective in the private realm also. To live, think and act in the private realm we must borrow words and ideas from the public. Hence the Marxist confidence that when religion is eliminated from the public realm it must in due course wither away in the private realm also.

And this surely is what is happening. In Western Europe the process has been confusingly long drawn out. As early as the 1690s it was already plain that the leading thinkers, in order to think new thoughts, were not transforming Christianity, but beginning to move out of it altogether. Since then religion has very slowly been forced out of the public realm, and, after being for a while privatized, has declined in the private realm too. In the Third World the process is vastly accelerated. Westernization, whether in the capitalist or communist form, is destroying ancient religious cultures very rapidly. There may be none left by the end of this century. Judaism (with its long experience of the ghetto), and Christianity (because of the Protestant movement) have learnt some of the arts of survival in privatized form. Christianity, in particular, is spreading very fast in the Third World because it is the religion best able to endure 'Westernization'. But the long-term outlook is not favourable. The lesson of history is that puritan dualism (with its compatibility-thesis) fails. The idea was that a secular, non-religious

[8] 'More Rumours of Angels', by David Hay.

science could have the public realm and the natural order, and that religion would be satisfied with the private realm of the individual conscience listening to God's revealed word. But the fact has been that private religion is slowly squeezed into emptiness and ineffectuality.

On the other side, however, there is something else to say. In the midst of its headlong expansion, science-based industrial society has run into acute difficulties:

(i) In the first place it is clear that the present rate of expansion cannot long be maintained. At the moment world population doubles about every forty years, and world energy-consumption every twenty years.[9] Bentley Glass reports from the U.S.A.[10] that for many decades the number of professional scientists has been doubling every twelve years, and the number of original published papers every fourteen years. The number of journals, and even the number of journals of abstracts, has similarly been growing exponentially, and so has the cost of scientific work. There is room for argument about how many people the world can support, at what rate of consumption, but it is surely beyond doubt that eventually there must be a transition to a steady state.

(ii) But that transition will be horribly painful, for it means an end to the secular eschatology (or, if you prefer, infantile illusion) of progress through linear time, and probably also an end to the restlessly creative, acquisitive and enquiring spirit of Western culture. At the moment it is hard to see these profound spiritual changes being made except by the forcible imposition of something like a Chinese world-view and Maoist politics.

(iii) Even while we are destroying ancient religious cultures we are coming to see more clearly how vital they are in giving symbolic meaning to life and binding society together. Artists can scarcely begin to describe the spiritual despair of young

[9] Barbara Ward and René Dubos, *Only One Earth* (Penguin 1972), pp. 42f.
[10] 'The Future of Science—Endless Horizons or the Golden Age?', in *Anticipation*, No. 10, February 1972 (Geneva, the W. C. C.), pp. 12ff. At the time of writing there is a severe world recession, but I assume that 'Western' countries intend to resume rapid economic growth if they have a chance to do so.

workers (and especially of the migrant-worker proletariat) in Western cities, and of the peasants of the Third World. We already see the need to preserve threatened plant and animal species, and we lament (though we cannot arrest) the disappearance of the remaining small tribal cultures. Now we are beginning to realize what a disaster is the destruction, proceeding apace during the 1970s, of most of Theravada Buddhism in South-East Asia.

The forces that are conspiring to eliminate religion from the world during the present century are so vast and so powerful that it is unthinkable that the religions themselves should be able to offer any serious resistance, and as yet they have not done so. The most that can be said is that here and there they have fought valiant rearguard actions. Thus Christianity survives in eastern Europe, though it can hardly be said to offer any serious challenge to the regime's world-view. Islam will not relinquish its hold on the Arabs easily, but there is a danger that (as may happen to Judaism in Israel) its religious content will be evacuated, and it will tend to become a mere racial ideology.

Yet mankind's need for religion is as great as ever, and it may be that the same enquiring spirit which has dissolved the old faiths may lead us in time to recover their now largely-lost message. It is encouraging that the study of religion has made such great progress over the last century.[11] The central and hardest issue remains that of cosmology, but even here we may be able to make some progress. The most destructive 'scientism' was never science alone, but science allied with blinkered philosophy (e.g., pp. 58f., above). Modern philosophy of science is less aggressive and absolutist in its claims (e.g., Chapter 7, above). The scientific cosmology is a great deal richer than it was (e.g., p. 38, above), a thought which I have taken further elsewhere.[12] In the seventeenth century 'final causes' were expelled from natural philosophy with the active approval of many religious men, but in the long run this severance of the natural order from the moral order

[11] A valuable handbook is W. A. Lessa and E. Z. Vogt, eds., *Reader in Comparative Religion: an Anthropological Approach*, 3rd edn New York, Harper and Row 1972.
[12] In the concluding essay in Hugh Montefiore, ed., *Man and Nature*. London, Collins 1975.

has threatened to destroy religion and man himself. The public moral order cannot survive without some cosmological foundation, but it matters a good deal what kind of foundation is here in question. Different religions can be defined in terms of the ways in which they make the connections between the natural order and the moral order. We pointed out (Chapter 2, and pp. 38f., above) that religions of redemption aspire beyond this present world-order; they draw symbols from the world to represent (however inadequately) a perfect good that lies beyond it, and is our final home.

DISCUSSION QUESTIONS

How far can political ideology perform the social functions historically performed by religion? In cases such as Nkrumahism, Nasserism, Maoism, etc., is it right to speak of the ideology as being 'religious'?

Consider the ways in which words like *law, attraction, energy, force, power*, etc., are used both in moral/social and in physical contexts. Does this suggest that physical science is still rather more anthropomorphic than it usually recognizes?

Responsible people are spending public money in trying to contact extra-terrestrial intelligences. Are the reasons for doing this scientific or religious or both? Are the extra-terrestrials basically the same as angels of the past?

FURTHER READING

(Books marked with an asterisk are for more advanced students only).

CHAPTER 1

The idea of two worlds or provinces has a long history. At one time it took the form of a distinction between the Book of Nature and the Book of Scripture. See Basil Willey, *The Seventeenth-Century Background*. London, Chatto and Windus 1934; and *Frank E. Manuel, *The Religion of Isaac Newton*. O.U.P. 1974. Its Victorian form owes much to Coleridge, Blake and Wordsworth. See David Newsome, *Two Classes of Men* (London, John Murray 1974), chapter 2. It persists in children's books, such as those of E. Nesbit and C. S. Lewis, and in the vogue for fantasy.

The controversies about evolution are introduced in the material published by the Open University in connection with its course, *Science and Belief: Copernicus to Darwin* AMST 283, Units 9-16, and the two set books edited by C. A. Russell and D. G. Goodman. Best of all is Darwin himself, in his books and correspondence.

CHAPTER 2

C. S. Lewis, *The Discarded Image*. C.U.P. 1964. Outlines of the scientific revolution of the seventeenth ceutury in *A. R. Hall, *From Galileo to Newton, 1630-1720*. London, Collins 1963; Hugh Kearney, *Science and Change, 1500-1700*. London, Weidenfeld and Nicolson 1971; *R. Hooykaas, *Religion and the Rise of Modern Science*. Edinburgh, Scottish Academic Press 1972;

and *A. Koyre, *From the Closed World to the Infinite Universe*. Baltimore, Johns Hopkins Press 1957.

There is no satisfactory book which looks generally at science and other religions: but there are valuable hints in *Joseph Needham's many-volumed *Science and Civilization in China*. C.U.P. 1954- .

CHAPTER 3

On cosmologies, see H. Frankfort, ed., *Before Philosophy*. Pelican 1949; *Mary Douglas, *Natural Symbols*. 2nd edn Pelican 1973; *Carmen Blacker and Michael Loewe, eds., *Ancient Cosmologies*. London, Allen and Unwin 1975; and the long series on the mythologies of various cultures published by Hamlyn.

European ideas of cosmic order can be sampled in *A. P. d'Entreves, *Natural Law*. London, Hutchinson 1951; and *A. O. Lovejoy, *The Great Chain of Being*. Harvard U.P. 1936; Harper Torchbook 1960.

CHAPTER 4

Charles Darwin, *The Descent of Man*. 1871; and *The Expression of the Emotions*. 1872; Charles Sherrington, *Man on His Nature*. O.U.P. 1940; *I. T. Ramsey, ed., *Biology and Personality*. O.U.P. 1965; *A. J. Ayer, 'Man as a Subject for Science', in *Metaphysics and Common Sense*. London, Macmillan 1969; and L. King, ed., *A History of Medicine*. Penguin 1971.

CHAPTER 5

D. F. Pears, ed., *Freedom and the Will*. London, Macmillan 1963; *R. L. Franklin, *Freedom and Determinism*. London, Routledge 1968; *J. R. Lucas, *The Freedom of the Will*. O.U.P. 1970; D. J. O'Connor, *Free Will*. New York, Anchor Books 1971; London, Macmillan 1972; and A. M. Farrer, *The Freedom of the Will*. London, A. & C. Black 1958. On Leibniz, there is now C. D. Broad's *Leibniz: An Introduction*. C.U.P. 1975.

CHAPTER 6

E. E. Evans-Pritchard, *Theories of Primitive Religion.* O.U.P. 1965; *V. W. Turner, *The Ritual Process.* U.S. edn, Aldine Pub. Co. 1969; Penguin 1974; *B. Malinowski, *Magic, Science and Religion and other Essays.* U.S. edn, Anchor Books 1948; London, Souvenir Press 1974; M. Douglas, *Purity and Danger.* London, Routledge 1966; Penguin 1970.

CHAPTER 7

Current views about the status of scientific knowledge can be pursued in *T. S. Kuhn, *The Structure of Scientific Revolutions.* University of Chicago Press 1962; *I. Lakatos and A. Musgrave, *Criticism and the Growth of Knowledge.* C.U.P. 1970; *Karl Popper, *Objective Knowledge.* O.U.P. 1972; and *Mary B. Hesse, *The Structure of Scientific Inference.* London, Macmillan 1974.

Comments from a science-and-religion viewpoint in Ian G. Barbour, *Myths, Models and Paradigms.* London, S.C.M. 1974.

CHAPTER 8

A good brief statement of orthodox dualism is Donald D. Evans, 'Differences between Scientific and Religious Assertions', in Ian G. Barbour, ed., *Science and Religion: New Perspectives on the Dialogue.* London, S.C.M. 1968. A. N. Whitehead's later books are still very stimulating and relevant, e.g., *Religion in the Making.* 1926; *Science and the Modern World.* 1926; and *Adventures of Ideas.* 1933. For Freud's views on religion and culture, see *Totem and Taboo.* 1913; *The Future of an Illusion.* 1928; and *Civilization and its Discontents.* 1930. The dates are those of the English translations.

INDEX

114

115

49895